"This marr
be easy. It
it's just not

"No," she laughed shakily, ... natural."

"But that doesn't mean we can't make it work. We just have to try harder."

"Niccolo, don't you think this has gone far enough? I'd thought you'd back off from the marriage discussion by now. You're not really going to go through with this."

"Oh, yes, *we* are."

"Maybe I'm misunderstanding you. Maybe you mean something in name only, an arrangement—"

"That would be convenient, wouldn't it?" he interrupted. "You have your baby, you have your safety net. Sorry, Maggie, our marriage would be *real*."

Shocked, she could only stare at him. A real marriage. Naked, beds, sex. Niccolo making love to her…

Jane Porter was born in California, USA, and spent her teens and early twenties living abroad. During her time in the UK, Jane discovered Mills & Boon® and read the books under the bedcovers so her mother wouldn't find out.

Now a teacher, with an MA in Writing, Jane lives in Seattle, with her husband and two small boys. She says she plots her books in between teaching her eldest son to read and changing her baby's nappies!

Please welcome Jane Porter to the Modern Romance™ series. THE ITALIAN GROOM, her first book, is the passionate and intensely moving story of Meg, a woman facing single motherhood until she moves back to her home town and is reunited with Nicco, the handsome idol of her teenage years. Like many Italian men, Nicco is protective and traditional—and he is determined that Meg should marry him, and let him be the father of her child...

THE ITALIAN GROOM

BY
JANE PORTER

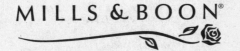

For my grandmother, Elizabeth.
I adore you. Jane

First published in Great Britain 2000
Harlequin Mills & Boon Limited,
Eton House, 18-24 Paradise Road, Richmond, Surrey TW9 1SR

© Jane Porter-Gaskins 2000

ISBN 0 263 82057 2

Set in Times Roman 10½ on 12 pt.
01-0201-42442

Printed and bound in Spain
by Litografia Rosés, S.A., Barcelona

CHAPTER ONE

"TEN years, and you still haven't changed." Niccolo's softly accented voice echoed with disgust, his sensual mouth flattening in anger. "You never would listen to reason—"

"Nic, I'm only asking for the spare set of keys to my parents' house," Meg interrupted, trying to ignore the churning in her stomach. "These are not trade secrets."

One of his black eyebrows lifted. "Is that a joke?"

She fought her fatigue and impatience. It wouldn't help to get into an argument with Nic. Nic would win. He always won.

Struggling to sound reasonable, she reminded him of the long-standing agreement between their families. "It's always been policy to keep a spare key for each other, in case of emergency. It's never been a problem before, and I don't know why you're making a big deal out of it now."

"Because it's not safe for you to stay alone at your parents'. The ranch is isolated. I'm ten minutes away if something should happen."

"Nothing will happen."

His voice fairly crackled with contempt. "Maggie, you attract trouble like pollen attracts bees. I've saved your skin from more scrapes—"

"I never asked for your help!"

"No, but you needed it."

"You don't know what I need, Nic. You just like

to think you do.'' She clenched her jaw, furious with herself for coming to the villa in the first place. If she hadn't misplaced the key ring to her parents' house, she wouldn't be having this conversation with Niccolo Dominici, nor would she be receiving another of his famous lectures.

He made a choking sound and muttered something in Italian.

''What was that?'' she demanded, knowing how he loved to resort to Italian when he wanted to say something particularly unflattering.

''I said I should give up on you.''

Meg stiffened indignantly, her shoulders squaring. She'd allowed him to crush her years ago, her tender heart broken by his harsh rejection, but thankfully she wasn't a teenager anymore. ''Then do! I don't need your so-called help.''

''So-called?'' He bristled, golden eyes glinting. The rapid pull of muscle in his jaw revealed her barb had hit home. She'd insulted him, bruising his considerable Italian machismo. Nic stared at her through narrowed eyes. ''You're fortunate that we have a very old friendship.''

''It's not much of a friendship,'' she retorted grimly. ''In fact, you're the last person I'd describe as a friend.''

His jaw tightened again, but he didn't answer her. Instead his eyes searched her face. She kept her expression purposely blank. She wouldn't give him the satisfaction of letting him see how strongly he still affected her. ''Give me the key.''

''No.''

''My parents know I'll be staying there. I left a message with the cruise line.''

"You cannot stay there alone."

"I *live* alone."

His mouth pinched tighter, and he crossed his arms, straining his green sport jacket. Yellow light glowed behind him, the villa's French doors open to embrace the warm California night. "Which is quite dangerous in New York. The city is full of strangers who prey on young women."

Inadvertently Mark, her baby's father, came to mind.

What was the expression? A wolf in sheep's clothing?

But she didn't want to think about Mark, didn't want to be reminded that she'd fallen for Mark partly because he'd reminded her so much of Niccolo. The fact that even after ten years Meg still desired men like Nic confounded her. Nic might be sinfully attractive, but he was also insufferably high-handed.

As it turned out, Mark and Nic were really nothing alike. Whereas Nic had scruples, Mark had none.

Mark wasn't just any old wolf, but a married wolf with three kids and a wife tucked in an affluent Connecticut neighborhood. Greenwich, to be precise.

Her stomach heaved at the memory. Mark had insisted she get rid of the baby, going so far as to make an appointment at a clinic, but Meg refused, and used the opportunity to head to California to get a start on her new landscape renovation.

Her stomach gurgled again, a squeamish reminder that it had been a long day and promised to be an equally long night. She was four and a half months into this pregnancy and still quite sick. She'd been prepared for nausea, but this…it felt like a flu that wouldn't end.

"I'm only in town for a few days," she said, bone-weary and beginning to feel a little desperate. "I'm meeting with clients till Thursday and then back to New York on Friday."

"It doesn't matter if you're only staying for a night. It's not safe."

Meg swallowed hard and fast. "I'll lock the door."

"No."

"Please."

"No."

"Nic, you're not my dad. And you're not Jared."

For a moment he said nothing, stunned to silence. Then the small muscle popped again in his jaw, revealing his tightly leashed temper. "Is that so?"

She swallowed her anger, appalled at what she'd said.

Of course he wasn't her brother. Nic had been her brother's best friend. Jared and Nic had been inseparable up until the minute Jared had crashed the car that one horrible Christmas Eve.

It was a terrible thing to say to Nic, and she took a frightened step back, hating herself for her unkindness. Silently she cursed her quick temper and even quicker tongue. There were times she wished she had a little of Niccolo's control.

"I'm sorry." She apologized, completely ashamed.

He nodded, his full lips pressed tight beneath his straight nose. She'd once teased him that he had a face Michelangelo would have loved. Nic had responded that he'd rather have been drawn by da Vinci. Something basic and spare. But there was nothing basic or spare about Niccolo. He was beautiful.

Repentant, she gazed at Nic, still horrified by her thoughtlessness. She'd struck below the belt and she knew it. Bile rose in her throat. She'd broken her cardinal rule. Any discussion of Jared and the accident was absolutely off-limits. "I shouldn't have said that about Jared—"

"It's okay. You're tired. It's late."

Instead of feeling relieved, she felt worse. "I don't want to fight with you. Please just let me have the key."

"There's a rash of robberies in the area lately. Nine local ranches and wineries have been hit. Last time an elderly woman, a very nice woman, was hurt. I can't let you take that risk."

Some of her anger dissipated. Meg's shoulders slumped wearily. So that was it. There'd been trouble in the area, and he was afraid for her. So like Niccolo. Still trying to protect her.

Meg turned and gazed across the villa's flagstone terrace to the magnificent view of the valley. In the moonlight the orderly row of grapes looked like olive green pinstripes against rounded hills.

In the ten years she'd been away, it seemed that nothing—not the grapes nor handsome, proud Niccolo—had changed. Oh, she'd been back a number of times, but she'd made it a point to visit when Nic was away. Somehow Nic and Jared and the past were so tangled together that she found it too painful to return home often.

"Who was hurt?" she asked, still drinking in the moonlit landscape. Unlike so many others, her parents used their fertile land for cattle and crops. Nic had once approached them about buying their acreage for top dollar. Her father had quietly but firmly refused. Nic had never brought the subject up again.

"Mrs. Anderson," he answered.

Her old piano teacher.

"How awful," Meg whispered.

"Which is why I can't let you go to your parents' home." Nic towered above her, exuding authority even in a casual sport coat and khaki trousers. "I've promised to look after your parents' place while they're gone. I know they wouldn't want you there, not after what happened to Mrs. Anderson."

"Of course." But she couldn't help a flash of disappointment. It was so late and she was so incredibly tired. It would have been wonderful to creep into bed in her old room with the nubby white chenille bedspread, the girlish ballet pictures on the wall, the row of Raggedy Anns on a shelf, and just sleep. To momentarily escape the exhaustion and her worry about the future and just be young Maggie again.

But young Maggie was long gone. When she left Healdsburg for college on the East Coast ten years ago, she'd vowed to make a new life for herself with people who didn't know her past or her name.

After finishing her studies Meg took a job with a prominent Manhattan landscape design firm, working her way up from fetching coffees to designing secret jewel-box gardens for Fifth Avenue mansions.

Meg knew she had a talent for design and was willing to work harder than anyone else in the firm. Which is how she'd landed the Hunt account in California. Actually, landed wasn't quite right. She'd fought for the job tooth and nail. The Hunts' garden renovation would take years and yet it would be the jewel in her crown. With the Hunt renovation on her résumé, she could open her own design firm, work from home, be independent.

Thus she'd squashed her apprehension about returning to Napa, resolving to give the Hunts the very best of her time and ability.

She'd be her own woman. She'd be her own boss. And she'd be a great mother, too.

Her convictions were undermined by moisture beading her brow, her nausea growing worse. "That's fine," she said, striving to sound casual. "I'll stay at a hotel tonight."

"That's absurd. I won't have you staying in a hotel. If you need a place to stay, you'll stay here."

The moisture on her skin felt cool and clammy. It was no longer a question of *if* she'd be sick, it was a question of *when*. "I don't want to put you out. There's a good hotel not far from here."

Quickly, she moved down the front steps toward her car, concentrating on every blue colored flagstone. *Just walk,* she told herself, *one foot and then the other. Don't let yourself get sick here. Don't do it. Don't do it.*

Niccolo's footsteps sounded behind her. She tried to hurry, practically running the last several feet. Just as she reached her car, he grabbed her arm and spun her around.

"Stop it!" Emotion vibrated in his voice. "Stop running away."

Her stomach heaved. Her forehead felt as if it were made of paste. Her mouth tasted sweet and sour. "This isn't the time for this."

His fingers gouged her arm, his grip tight and punishing. "Will there ever be a good time? We haven't talked in ten years. I haven't seen you since you ran away the last time. Why does it have to be like this?''

"Nic."

"What?"

"I'm going to be sick.''

He passed a fresh facecloth to her in the bathroom. Meg gratefully accepted the cool, damp cloth and placed it against her temple. She leaned against the bathroom sink, her legs still weak, her hands shaking. "Thank you.''

"You should have told me you weren't well.''

His gruffness drew a lopsided smile. This was Niccolo at his most compassionate. She ought to be grateful for small mercies. Fortunately the facecloth hid her smile. It would only infuriate him. "I'm fine,'' she breathed, her voice still quivering. "Just tired, but nothing that a good night's sleep won't fix.''

"You're not one to throw up when you're tired.''

Lifting her head slightly, she met his eyes. His expression unnerved her. There was nothing gentle in his cool golden gaze.

She buried her face in the damp cloth again. "It was a long trip,'' she said. "I haven't eaten much today.''

She couldn't tell him that sometimes just the smell of food made her stomach empty and that lately, Mark's relentless pressure had killed what little remained of her appetite. Mark's constant phone calls had changed in tone, becoming increasingly aggressive as she refused to cooperate with his plans. Mark made it sound so simple. Just terminate the pregnancy. That was all there was to it.

Meg trembled inwardly, furious. Terminate the pregnancy, indeed! As if her baby was an appointment or an insurance policy.

She couldn't tell Niccolo any of this. Instead she answered glibly something about not having enough time. His brows drew together. His expression was severe.

"When did you arrive in Napa?" he asked.

"I flew into San Francisco this morning." She lifted her head, her hands resting against the cool porcelain of the sink. The sink was imported from Italy, like nearly everything in the stone villa. "The flight was delayed—fog, I think it was—so I drove straight up to make my appointment on time."

"You couldn't call and let your appointment know you needed a lunch break?"

"I bought a sandwich at the airport."

"Cuisine at its finest." His lovely mouth curled derisively and she sat back, still fascinated by the faint curve of his lips. That one night she'd kissed him years ago burned in her memory. He kissed the way she'd imagined he would. Fiercely. With passion. Not at all the way boys her own age kissed.

"Francesca is in the kitchen putting something together for you," he continued. "She had fresh tomatoes and little shrimp she thought would be perfect."

Fresh shrimp? Meg's stomach churned. She'd never be able to eat shrimp. "Really. That's not necessary."

Nic's expression darkened. "Don't tell that to Francesca. She's got three pots on the stove and is singing in Italian. You'd think we were having a midnight dinner party from the way she's carrying on.'' He turned and leaned against the doorjamb. ''But then, she's always had a soft spot for you. You *are* part of the family.''

''Even if I don't call or write for ten years?'' She'd meant to be flippant, but Nic didn't crack a smile.

''I don't laugh at your bad jokes.''

He could be so stuffy sometimes. She wrinkled her nose and rolled her eyes. ''It's not really a bad joke. I think it's more your mood—''

''You see, *cara*, I did call,'' he interrupted smoothly. ''I wrote, too. I wrote to you at your university. Then later when you had your first apartment. Even during the year you spent in London, as an apprentice for Hills and Drake Design.''

Her legs suddenly felt shaky again, and she sat down rather heavily on the edge of the toilet. ''Yes, you wrote me. You wrote pages and pages in the harshest tone imaginable.'' His censure had hurt, hurt terribly. ''Of course I didn't answer your letters! You were cruel—''

''I've never been cruel to you.''

''Nic, you humiliated me!''

''You humiliated yourself. I still don't understand what you were thinking, climbing on my lap, acting like a—a...''

''Say it.''

He visibly recoiled. ''Never mind.''

She balled up the facecloth in her hands, frustrated with his rigid views. Poor, proper Nic raised to view girls as helpless creatures and boys as inheritors of the earth.

''I won't apologize for that evening,'' she told

him, blood surging to her cheeks. "I'll never apologize. I did nothing wrong."

"*Cara,* you weren't wearing panties."

Her face burned and yet she tilted her head, defiant. She'd been crazy about him, utterly infatuated, and she'd desperately wanted to impress him. "I'd read it was considered sexy."

"You were a schoolgirl."

"I was seventeen."

"Sixteen."

"Almost seventeen."

"And you were wearing a white lace—what do you call it?"

"Garter belt."

"Yes, garter belt beneath your skirt. White lace garter belt and no panties. What was I supposed to think?"

It was beyond his ability to see her as anything but Jared's kid sister. "That I liked you, Nic. That I had a teenage crush and I was trying to impress you." She stood up and tossed the crumpled facecloth at him.

He caught the damp cloth, knuckling it. "It didn't impress me. It made me sick."

This was exactly why she hadn't answered his letters. He didn't understand how harsh he'd been. How harsh he could be. Niccolo had been raised in a wealthy, aristocratic Italian family. His values were old-world, old-school, and despite the fact that he embraced much of the American culture, he still believed a woman's virtue was by far her most precious asset. Instead of being flattered by her attempt at seduction, he'd been appalled. Appalled and disgusted.

Meg stood up, catching a glimpse of herself in the

vanity mirror. Shadows formed blue crescents beneath her eyes. Her dark curls had come loose from their twisted knot, creating inky tendrils around her pale face.

She turned from the mirror, too tired and worn out to make an attempt at smoothing her stray curls. "This won't work, Nic. Let me go to a hotel. Francesca will understand."

He stopped her as she tried to step past him, catching her by the hand, his fingers sliding up to capture her wrist. He held her closely against him, just as he had when she was younger and needing comfort after Jared died.

"But I won't understand," he murmured. "I don't know what's happened to us. I don't know why you're so angry with me. You can't even talk to me without spitting and hissing like a frustrated kitten."

She didn't hear his words, only felt his warmth. She'd forgotten how sensitive he made her feel, as if her limbs were antennae, her skin velvet-covered nerve endings. It was a dizzying sensation to be so close to him, intense and dazzling. He might have been Jared's best friend but he didn't feel like Jared. He didn't feel like a brother at all.

Her heart thumped painfully hard, and for a second she longed to wrap her arms around him, to seek the warmth she'd once found in him.

Before she could speak, Francesca, the housekeeper of the last thirty three years, appeared, wiping her hands on a white apron.

"Dinner's ready," Francesca announced, beaming with pleasure. "Come, Maggie, I've made you a special pasta, very light, very fresh. I think you will like it very much. Please. Come. Sit down."

*   *   *

The kitchen smelled of olive oil and garlic. Francesca had set two places at the rough-hewn pine table near the massive stone fireplace. A fire crackled in the hearth, and the fat beeswax pillar candles on the table glowed with light.

"Smells wonderful," Meg said, surprised that the scent of garlic and onion didn't turn her stomach. She sniffed again, checking for a fishy smell or a hint of shrimp, but nothing rankled her nose. In fact, her stomach growled with hunger. But then, Francesca had always been an incredible cook. She could make the simplest ingredients taste exquisite.

Niccolo held a chair out for her, and Meg took a seat at the table.

"Everything is very fresh," Francesca said again, serving the bowls of pasta and presenting them at the table. "I remember you like olives in your pasta, and these are just perfect. Clean and sweet, not bitter."

Nic opened a bottle of Dominici red from his private reserve. They ate in near silence, making small talk about the weather and the local wines.

Meg was grateful that Nic steered the conversation away from personal topics, and gradually her tension headache began to ease.

The phone rang down the hall. Although it was close to midnight, Francesca answered it. "The papa," she said, returning to the kitchen.

"My father," Nic said, standing. "I must take this call."

"Of course," Meg answered, breaking her crusty roll. She knew that with the time difference between California and Florence, Nic did a lot of business late at night. The Dominici family owned wineries in Italy and northern California. Niccolo was in charge of the California winery. His father and younger brother managed the Italian estates.

Francesca waited until Nic was gone to approach Meg. She didn't waste any time with small talk. Instead she gave Meg a long, considering look. Meg shifted uncomfortably, avoiding the housekeeper's eyes.

Tension mounted. Francesca didn't move.

Finally Meg dropped the crusty roll on her plate and wiped her fingers on her napkin. "Yes, Francesca?"

"You're pregnant, aren't you?"

"No." The denial was so automatic, the response so instinctive, that Meg didn't even consider admitting the truth.

The housekeeper clucked and shook her head. "Do your parents know?"

"They've been on vacation."

"So you are pregnant." Francesca folded her hands across her middle. "You came to the right place. Niccolo will take care of you."

"No! No, Francesca, that's not even an option. Nic and I…no. Absolutely not."

The housekeeper looked offended. "What's wrong with my Niccolo?"

"Nothing's wrong with Nic, but this isn't his problem." More firmly, she said, "I'm doing very well. I don't need help."

"But you're not married."

"I don't have to be married to have a baby."

Francesca's displeasure showed. "You don't know anything about babies. It's not easy being a mother. I know."

"I'll learn." Meg pushed back from the table.

"I've always wanted children. This is a good thing. I'm not ashamed."

"So why won't you tell him?"

"Tell me what?" Nic asked from the doorway. He took his seat at the large pine table and glanced from his housekeeper to Meg. "What should I know?"

Meg raised her chin. "About my new job working with the Hunts."

He shot the housekeeper a quick glance. Francesca shrugged and turned away. Nic looked at Meg. "Your job?" he prompted.

"Yes," Meg answered, sending a wary glance in Francesca's direction. "With the Hunts. They're interested in renovating their gardens."

Pots suddenly banged in the deep cast-iron sink.

Meg raised her voice. "It's a century-old estate." More pots crashed. Meg winced but bravely continued. "I've spent the last year courting them. I really wanted this opportunity—"

"Francesca." Niccolo's reproach silenced the pot banging. The housekeeper shrugged and turned to other tasks. "Please, *cara*," he said to Meg, "finish your story."

"It's not really a story. It's just my job." And the opportunity of a lifetime, she mentally added.

"Your parents mentioned that the Hunts interviewed six landscape designers, but you were the only American."

"Flattering, isn't it?"

"They picked you."

"Yes." She couldn't hide her pride, or her pleasure. The Hunt gardens were among the finest in California. "I'm thrilled. This isn't just work, it's a dream. Ever since I was a little girl I've been fascinated with the Hunt estate. I remember creeping around their hedges, hiding in the old maze. Their gardens were magical, and now I have a chance to work new magic.''

''Is that who you were meeting with today?''

''Yes. I'll be meeting with them for the next several months. I'll commute back and forth from New York. It'll be quite an intensive project.''

Nic raised his wineglass. ''To you, *cara*. I'm proud of you. This is really quite an achievement.''

She raised her glass, and Niccolo clinked goblets with her, the fine crystal tinging. But instead of sipping the wine she set her goblet down and took another bite from her pasta.

''You're not drinking?'' Niccolo set his goblet down.

Of course he'd notice something like that. He was a winegrower. He made some of the finest table wines in California. ''I have to be up early,'' she answered. ''I'll need to be sharp.''

''Of course,'' he murmured, his eyes fixed on her.

Francesca suddenly turned from the sink. ''I'll make a lunch for you tomorrow. A roll, some fruit, meat and cheese. You like yogurt, yes? I shall send a yogurt, too, that way you can nibble whenever your stomach doesn't feel so good.''

Meg remembered the picnic lunches the housekeeper used to pack for them when they were kids. They were the best sack lunches in the world. ''Thank you, Francesca,'' she said, touched by the housekeeper's kindness. ''I'd like that very much, as long as it's no trouble.''

''No trouble at all,'' Francesca answered stoutly. ''You're family. You will always be family.''

It was the same thing Niccolo had said earlier.

This time the words evoked a rush of longing so intense that Meg's eyes nearly filled with tears. She was suddenly reminded of the years come and gone and the pain they'd all shared when Jared died that horrible Christmas and Maggie had taken the blame. For a split second she wished she could go back through time and make it the way it once was, but that was an impossible wish. Jared was gone, and her friendship with Niccolo had never been the same.

"Thank you, Francesca," Meg answered softly. "Have a good night."

"Seeing you again makes it a good night."

Despite her protests, Niccolo walked with her to her car to claim her overnight bag. "You're not worried I'm going to sneak away, are you?"

The corner of Nic's mouth lifted wryly. "No. I have your parents' house key here," he said, patting his sport jacket.

"You don't trust me."

"Should I?"

"I'm wearing panties, I promise."

"These jokes…I don't find them funny at all."

She stood up on tiptoe and patted his cheek. He smelled like oranges and sandalwood, decidedly Roman. He had his fragrance made for him on the Continent. Another little luxury he took for granted. "You never did, Nic. I drove you crazy even when I was eleven."

His golden eyes glinted in the moonlight. She thought he looked troubled, almost sad. He gazed at her, taller by a full head and shoulders. His thick hair hung long enough to brush his collar. He'd always worn his hair long. It was more European, and it suited his features. Niccolo might own a home in northern California, but he was pure Italian. Old-world Italian, at that.

"You look thin," he said, after a moment. "Are you starving yourself?"

"You only date broomsticks, Nic. How can I be too thin?"

His mouth curved, transforming his darkly handsome face into something impossibly beautiful. She suddenly wondered if he knew how devastating his smile was. He had to know.

She tried to picture him practicing his smile at the mirror but failed. Niccolo didn't practice charm. It just happened. He wore his strength and elegance as if it were one of his Armani suits.

"But you're Maggie," he answered, his smile fading. "You're not meant to be a broomstick."

He still didn't understand that she'd grown up. She was certain he only saw the sixteen-year-old hellion when he looked at her. "I'm twenty-eight, Niccolo, and I'm not Maggie anymore. I go by Meg."

"No."

"Yes. Meg or Margaret, take your pick."

His brow furrowed, his upper lip curled. She reached up and pressed two fingers against his lips. "Oh, Nic, don't. That's an awful face."

"But you give me such awful choices, *cara*," he said against her fingertips.

Her fingers tingled, and she pulled them away. "But those are your choices. Meg or Margaret."

"Never Margaret. You're not a Margaret. And Meg? That sounds like a seasoning. I prefer Maggie.

It fits you. Quick, lovely, unpredictable. That's my Maggie.''

A bittersweet emotion filled her. "Am I lovely?''

He didn't immediately answer, considering her question. Then deliberately he tilted her face up, studying her in the moonlight. The intensity in his gaze stole her breath. "More lovely than you have the right to be after all the heartache you've caused me.''

"I've caused *you* heartache?'' She felt her mouth tremble. Hope and pain blistered her heart. She hated the complexity of her emotions. It wasn't fair. Her world had changed. She had changed, and yet here she was, still so drawn to Niccolo.

His palm felt rough against her jaw. The pad of his thumb lightly caressed her cheek. "More than you'll ever know.''

CHAPTER TWO

NICCOLO tramped across a half acre of his vineyard, his Western-style boots crunching the ground. The air felt crisp, exhilarating, and he breathed in the richness of the early fall morning.

Even though it had been years since he helped harvest the grapes, Nic still inspected the crops every morning. An excellent wine required more than sun, rain, good soil; it needed passion. While the Dominici family had numerous business ventures, the Dominici wines and extensive vineyards were Niccolo's passion.

Passion.

The word immediately brought Maggie to mind, and as he thought of her, his mouth curved wryly.

Maggie wasn't easy. She tended to arouse fierce emotions in people. Some admired her, others disliked her, but either way, you had an opinion.

Frankly, like Jared, he'd adored her. Maggie had been an irresistible little girl. A scamp, really. She created more mischief than a dozen children put together. Yet her antics amused him, just as she amused him, her dark curls and expressive eyes arousing his protective instinct as if he really were another big brother.

He'd helped teach her to drive, escorted her to a high school dance, tutored her in calculus. When she'd had a falling out with her parents, she'd asked him to intercede. When she had been kicked out of class for arguing with a teacher, Niccolo was the one to pick her up from school.

Maggie.

Hotheaded, impulsive, passionate Maggie.

His smile faded. If only she hadn't pulled that silly prank and tried to seduce him. Even now he felt uncomfortable when he thought about that evening. She'd shocked him by sliding onto his lap and passionately kissing him. Her openmouthed kiss, the flick of her tongue. Nic's jaw tightened.

He'd tried to push her away, but she'd clung to him. When he attempted to lift her off his lap, he'd encountered a bare thigh and a very naked bottom.

He should have laughed about it. Should have made a joke, teased her or something. But he hadn't been able to. He'd been responding to her kiss and her warmth. His desire had mortified him. Nic had thrown her off his lap and said something far harsher than he intended. She'd looked stunned. She'd stood there clutching the hem of her schoolgirl skirt, trying not to cry.

Then she'd left. He should have gone after her, should have tried to talk to her. But his pride and shame wouldn't let him. He'd told himself she owed him an apology. He'd convinced himself that she just needed time, and truthfully, they both did.

Niccolo headed toward the house, periodically stopping to inspect the new vines he'd planted last spring at the base of a massive trellis. These were his newest additions to his grapes, and he checked for frost damage on the tender shoots, but happily found none.

With Maggie away at college, Niccolo had begun to feel the loss of her company. Healdsburg was a sleepy little town and without Jared and Maggie, California lost its charm. Niccolo returned to Florence for a second business degree and to help his father run the vast Tuscany vineyards.

He'd learned a great deal working with his father and brother. Four years later his father had approached him, asking if Niccolo would be interested in managing the Napa Valley vineyards and overseeing the California businesses. Niccolo had jumped at the opportunity. He wanted to experiment with new grape varieties and dreamed of producing a California Chianti reserve with the family's Tuscany grapes.

Nic neared the house, reaching the corner terrace with the arbor trellis. In mild weather he ate his breakfast on the sunny terrace. Francesca had already laid a light breakfast on the wrought-iron table. He took a seat, opened the paper.

The French doors opened, and Maggie appeared. As their eyes met, he felt an inexplicable spark of awareness. He suddenly remembered how it felt to hold Maggie. Touching her was like grasping a live wire. She was nothing short of electric.

"Good morning, Nic."

Her voice, smooth, soft, quiet, made him feel disturbingly unquiet. He folded his paper, aware of the distance between them. "Good morning, *cara*. How did you sleep?"

She smiled at him, but her smile looked forced. "Surprisingly well. The bed in the guest room is heavenly."

She held her briefcase. Her travel bag hung from her shoulder. She'd packed. "So why leave?"

For a moment Maggie appeared at a loss for

words. Then she wrinkled her nose, a trait left over from her childhood. "It's easier, Nic. Less complicated."

"You're worried you're forming an unhealthy attachment to the bed?"

The corner of her mouth quirked. "You sound like a therapist."

"I dated one once."

"When?"

"Last year. Alas, it did not work. Anna felt competitive with the grapes. She asked me to choose."

"Oh, Nic!"

"I know. How could she ask such a thing?"

"No, Niccolo. How terrible for her. She obviously didn't know you or she wouldn't have posed the question."

"You wouldn't make me choose?" he teased.

"No, I know better. You're in love with your grapes. You always have been." She turned from him to gaze across the golden hills marked by rows of neat green vines. Lifting her face to the rising sun, Maggie closed her eyes. "Nowhere else smells like this. Mornings smell so new."

He couldn't take his eyes off her, awash in ambivalent emotions. On one hand he wanted to protect her, the old big-brother instinct. But there was another instinct, one far more primitive, one colored by a hunger he didn't quite understand. "The mornings are my favorite, too."

Maggie opened her eyes and smiled at him. "I can't believe how much I've missed this place. I've even missed you."

"What a painful admission," he answered dryly.

She made a face at him, shifting her briefcase to

the other hand. ''You're lucky, you know. You're lucky you love this land and find so much happiness with the vineyard. Most people don't love what they do.''

He crossed the terrace to stand beside her, gazing at the same view. The land rolled and undulated like burnished waves, acres of vines contrasting with the white and gold hills. ''Is it just me you've avoided, Maggie, or is it more?''

He felt her tense, and glancing at her profile, he noticed the tears on her black lashes, delicate tears of love and longing and not quite buried pain.

''How can anyone love a place and yet hate it at the same time? How can such a good place be so brutal?'' Her voice quivered with passion.

''The land didn't kill your brother.''

''No, but it took him anyway.''

He didn't contradict her. Even now he couldn't drive the back road where Jared had crashed without feeling anger and loss. And guilt. Guilt that Jared had been the one at the wheel. Guilt that he'd survived and Jared died. Guilt that Maggie had taken the blame for Jared's mistake. He knew better than anyone that the accident had nearly destroyed Maggie's parents.

He glanced down at her bent head. ''I still miss him.''

She tried to smile through her film of tears. ''Thank you.''

''Do not thank me. I loved your brother.''

She bit her lip, working the flesh between her teeth. He could feel her silent pain, and it tore at him. ''Your brother was my closest friend. He was more of a brother to me than my own.''

"Mom and Dad don't talk about him anymore. I know it's painful for them, but I miss saying Jared's name. I miss hearing stories about him."

"You can always talk about him to me. I like to remember him, too. I like to remember the good times." Then he lifted the travel bag off her shoulder. "So you will stay tonight. It's decided."

"Nic—"

"We agreed last night that this was the best place for you to stay."

"We didn't agree. You told me to stay. That's different than me agreeing."

He tried to keep a straight face. "Must be a translation problem."

"Your English is perfect. So is your tendency to dominate. Which is why it'd be better if I stayed somewhere else. I don't need to quarrel with you. I have too much on my mind."

He merely smiled. Maggie had never been easy. "Agreed. Now, come sit down and tell me about your work. I'm anxious to learn more about the Hunt gardens."

She wrinkled her nose again, obviously skeptical. "You don't like gardening, Nic. You only care about grapes and wine."

"That's not true. I'm very proud of the Dominici gardens."

"The only reason you have gorgeous gardens is your grandfather and mother labored over them for nearly forty years. You'd plow the whole thing under if you thought you could get away with it."

"But I'd put the soil to good use."

"Pinot noirs, perhaps?"

He chuckled, delighted. She might have grown up,

but she was still feisty, still spirited. "They're certainly easier on the tongue than topiaries."

She laughed, just as he intended, and he felt a rush of tenderness. Jared had once said there were two ways to change Maggie's mood—tease her or kiss her. Either worked to diffuse her notoriously quick temper.

Tease her or kiss her.

Niccolo gazed at Maggie's mouth. She was wearing sheer lipstick, a soft shade that suited her dark hair and fair complexion. Despite the elegant cut of her blue tailored jacket and the thick strand of pearls around her neck, she looked far from cool, definitely not conservative. It was her mouth that betrayed her warmth. Her lips were lush, her upper lip bowed, a mouth made for champagne, dark chocolate and lovemaking.

Niccolo sucked in air, stunned by the thought. Make love to Maggie? Never. She might not be a girl anymore, but she was still young, still inexperienced. He cared for her deeply, but his feelings were platonic. She was the sister he'd never had.

He was resolved that nothing would come between them again. He refused to let their relationship change. She needed him, and he needed her. Period.

Francesca opened the door and emerged balancing a silver tray with pots of hot coffee and warm milk.

He seated Maggie, and Francesca poured her café au lait, heavy on the milk.

"Would you prefer less milk?" he asked Maggie, noticing Francesca's heavy handed pouring.

"She likes milk," Francesca answered firmly, passing a platter of sliced melon and another of warm pastries. "Milk is good for her."

Niccolo didn't comment and Maggie lifted her coffee cup, inhaling the steam and fragrant blend. "I've tried to give this up, but I can't. I love good coffee too much. One cup every morning, that's my limit, yet I do enjoy it."

"If coffee is your only vice, you're doing quite well, *cara*."

"It all depends on your definition of vice, doesn't it?" she answered.

He noticed the delicate pink blush staining her cheeks, her coloring so fine that even a hint of a blush made her vivid, exquisite.

"*Amore*, you've grown up. I don't see how you could possibly have a vice."

She shook her head, biting her lower lip. He stared at the soft lip with fascination and almost envy. There was so much sweetness in her, sweetness and mystery.

"I'm having guests tonight. A dinner party that's been planned for months. I'm introducing my new Chianti. It's one of the first American Chianti ever made with Tuscany grapes. I hope you'll be free to join us."

Meg's second day with the Hunts was again spent in deep discussion. Though the Hunts were committed to renovating their century-old gardens, they found it painful to discuss removing aging trees even though they understood many of the older trees were diseased and dying. Most of the afternoon was spent working through their concerns and acknowledging their sorrow at losing such majestic trees.

Their great devotion to the land was something she understood. Meg sometimes felt trapped in New York, even though she'd chosen for business purposes to make it her home. There were times when all the concrete and asphalt made her head spin. Too much noise, too much smog, too much activity.

Perhaps that's why she'd channeled her love of gardens into a career. People needed places of refuge. Sanctuary from the busy, modern world. Trees, shade, cool green places, these could restore one's soul.

Meg's eyebrows arched at her archaic word. *Soul.* It wasn't a very modern notion, and yet nearly everyone called her a very modern woman. Especially her father. But when her father called her modern, he didn't mean it as a compliment.

Her eyebrows arched even higher as she imagined his reaction to the news of the baby. He'd be upset, angry, disappointed—but not surprised. Certainly not surprised. He'd come to expect the worst from her. He almost expected her to fail him again.

Meg flexed her hands against the steering wheel, miserably aware that her cool relationship with her father was about to get colder.

She pulled into the formal gates leading to the Dominici villa. Valet drivers waved her over. She'd forgotten all about Niccolo's dinner party, and approaching the stucco and stone house, she heard the sweet plaintive notes of a violin. The Dominicis always mixed music and wine.

Meg hesitated outside the massive front door, listening to the string quartet. It was gorgeous music. A piece by Pachelbel. The brighter notes were tempered by an underlying longing. Much like her own emotions.

Jared. Her father. Niccolo. Everything here felt so complicated. Coming home was the hardest thing she knew how to do. There was a reason she avoided Napa Valley, and suddenly she was in the thick of it, caught up in the intensity and the memories and sorrow. If it weren't for the Hunts, she'd grab her suitcase and catch the nearest plane to New York. Right now the noise and glare of Manhattan seemed infinitely more palatable than this muddle of emotion.

The Pachelbel piece ended, and Meg shook off her melancholy mood. She was here to work, not to continuously examine her feelings.

Meg discovered Niccolo in the great room that had been designed as a ballroom. It was Niccolo's favorite room for large parties and winery-related entertaining.

Although Francesca was present, tuxedo-attired waiters served the catered appetizers. Offered a tray of toasted Brie rounds, Meg accepted one and nibbled on it, watching Nic mingle with his guests. He wore a pale green suit and a crisp white shirt. The shirt was open at the neck, revealing a hint of his broad chest, his skin golden from hours in the sun.

He laughed at something one of his guests said, throwing his head back, his dark hair brushing his collar. Supremely male, Meg thought, as he turned to greet another guest. Beautiful, sleek. Powerful.

Suddenly he was looking at her. Their eyes met, and slowly one corner of his mouth lifted in recognition. She felt a bubble of warmth form inside her chest and she smiled back, pleased.

He broke free from the circle of guests and moved through the crowd toward her. Meg balanced the remains of the toasted round on a paper napkin, her appetite gone.

His arms encircled her. His face dipped. Her nose was pressed against the exposed skin at the base of his throat. She felt his pulse and the heat of his chest.

A tremor coursed through her as he lifted her chin, kissing both cheeks. "Maggie, *cara*, when did you arrive?"

He held her loosely, and yet she was aware of the length of him, his taut hips inches from hers, his strong chest brushing her breasts. Her nipples tingled. She tingled. "Just a bit ago," she answered breathlessly, disposing of the appetizer on a server's empty tray.

It was crazy to respond to him like this. She knew how he felt about her, knew he wasn't attracted to her, and yet her body ignored her brain and flooded her limbs with warmth, filling her with a hot, languid need that had nothing to do with reason and everything to do with desire.

"You look tired," he said, brushing a tendril from her cheek.

"Do I?" She reached up to pat her French twist, feeling better than she had in days. She hadn't felt all that tired until now. In fact, she hadn't been queasy once today. "Perhaps I should go upstairs and put on some lipstick."

"Not to worry, you look lovely. Now come, let me introduce you around."

Dinner was delicious, and Niccolo's guests were interesting, but by ten o'clock Meg had slipped away from the festivities to her room.

The guest wing in Niccolo's stone villa offered elegant sanctuary, and after a long soak in the sunken tub, and after lathering lotion on her skin, Meg pulled on her cotton nightshirt and sat at the dressing table.

Mark hated her roomy blue striped nightshirt. She'd taken it with her on their one and only weekend getaway. Later he'd gone out and bought her a satin and feather concoction that made her giggle. She remembered holding the scrap of fabric to the light. "Mark, what on earth is this?"

"You don't like it," Mark had answered flatly, his feelings obviously injured.

"It's not that I don't like it, it's just not *me*."

Mark had told her to take it back and carelessly tossed the sales receipt at her. Realizing she'd hurt him, she'd tried to appease him. They'd ended up in bed.

They'd kissed before, but never made love. It was the first time they'd been so intimate, as well as the last. But once was more than enough. They'd made a baby, a baby Mark refused to acknowledge.

"There's been no one else," she'd told him, horrified that he even suggested she'd been sleeping around.

"I don't care," he'd answered bitterly. "I don't want this baby. You can't keep it."

"You're just angry."

"I'm not angry. Because I know you'll do the right thing—"

"Right thing?" she'd challenged.

"Yes, the right thing. This baby isn't an option." It was then he'd confessed he was married. He'd said he loved his wife and he didn't want to hurt her and that if Meg kept the baby, it would ruin his life.

Ruin his life.

Her eyes burned, and she picked up the hairbrush, gritting her teeth to keep from crying out.

How dared he? How could anyone be so self-absorbed?

His life. What about their baby's life?

Meg dragged the brush through her hair until her scalp tingled and her arm grew weary, refusing to stop until her anger subsided.

Thank goodness she'd never loved him. For a short time, she'd imagined she did. He'd looked so much like Niccolo, his Greek mother giving him the same hard features and dark coloring, but he lacked Nic's strength of character, not to mention Nic's morals.

Nic would never sleep around. Nic would take responsibility for his child.

Meg stilled, the brush hovering in midair. She had to stop doing that. Had to stop comparing every man to Nic. It wasn't fair to other men, and goodness, it wasn't fair to her. She'd never meet the right man if she continued to hold Niccolo up as some standard for manhood.

A knock sounded on her bedroom door.

Meg set the brush down and opened the door. Francesca stood in the doorway, hands on hips. "I saw your light still on. I thought you might not be well. How are you feeling?"

"I'm fine."

"You left the party early."

"Niccolo didn't mind."

Five minutes later, just as Meg prepared to slip into bed, there came another knock on her door. She opened the door a second time.

Niccolo stood in the doorway balancing a cup and saucer and a small plate of cookies.

Meg didn't think she had the energy to smile, but her lips twitched anyway. "Housekeeping?"

"You're not funny."

"I'm very funny. You just have a terrible sense of humor."

His lovely mouth grimaced. "This was not my idea."

"Obviously. You know I hate warm milk."

"The point is, I will not be making a habit of bringing you bedtime snacks."

She didn't know why, but his gruffness compelled her to tease him. "Are you sure this wasn't your idea? You know I'm a sucker for cookies."

"They're biscuits."

"Cookies, biscuits, same thing."

"They're not at all the same."

"Like comparing apples and oranges."

"No, not like apples and oranges. Like a Merlot and a Cabernet."

"Of course. Wine. That's all you ever think about."

Niccolo's expression darkened. She'd succeeded in aggravating him. "Do you like quarreling with me?"

Meg smiled impudently. "Yes."

He muttered beneath his breath in Italian. "You test my patience."

"Then don't let me keep you."

"You're not keeping me. I'm choosing to stand here."

"That's right, you always have to win. Even if it's just a war of words."

"And you have to argue. You're still such a child."

Meg's stomach began to cramp. Perhaps it wasn't the Brie that had made her sick. It was Nic. "Like I said, don't let me keep you." With that she slammed the door shut, ignoring the surprised expression on Niccolo's face.

Meg twitched in her seat, trying to keep still. She'd never been bored by a discussion on perennials in her life, but at the moment, she thought she'd scream if deadheading was mentioned again.

She closed her eyes, pressed her knuckles against her brow and forced herself to draw a deep breath and slowly exhale. One yarrow, two yarrow, three yarrow…counting yellow yarrow the way one would count sheep.

Some of the tension left her shoulders. Meg drew another deep breath and opened her eyes. She'd woken up feeling blue, and the blue mood quickly turned to irritation. All morning her nerves had been on edge, and Mr. Hunt's rather long-winded discourse on deadheading had just about driven her mad.

What she needed was action.

She had a hundred and one things to decide, plans to make, and this discussion on gardening chores was getting her nowhere.

What she needed was a new apartment.

She'd been living in a quaint one-bedroom flat across from Central Park for years. The apartment had a squeaky hardwood floor, antiquated plumbing and a charming little terrace with a breathtaking city view. But the apartment barely accommodated her bed and sitting room furniture, much less a crib and changing table.

Yes, she needed a bigger apartment.

She also needed a crib. A car seat. High chair. A layette, not to mention diapers, ointment, powders and so forth.

Babies certainly required a lot of gear.

No wonder her old college friends had complained about babies being expensive. Meg would need a small fortune to outfit the baby's room, much less pay for child care while she met with clients.

She couldn't blame anyone but herself. She'd slept with Mark knowing the risks. He'd used a condom, but things did happen and, well, things *had* happened.

A nerve pulsed at Meg's temple and she pressed two fingers against the spot, trying hard to stay calm, to sit still.

The truth was, becoming a single mother terrified her.

It was such a huge responsibility, such a crucial role, she couldn't help being afraid. Meg had made her share of mistakes and she knew she'd make them as a mother. Her baby deserved the very best, but what if Meg wasn't good enough? Strong enough? Loving enough? What if she said the wrong thing, forgot the right prayer? What if…

"Margaret?" Mrs. Hunt leaned forward to clasp Meg's hand. "Margaret, dear, are you all right? You're looking quite pale."

She was fine. She was just a little nervous. But that was only to be expected. Even for a modern woman, having a baby was quite a big deal.

Niccolo glanced at his watch. The winery co-op council meeting should have wrapped up just after lunch. Instead it threatened to last well into mid afternoon. He shot a quick glance at his watch. He had another hour before he'd have to excuse himself.

The local wineries had formed a co-op to promote northern California wines. The council was in the final stages of planning and implementing an international advertising campaign highlighting Napa's outstanding red wines.

The television and print advertisements would feature the Italian film star Sonia Carlo sipping a California Cabernet. It was hoped her celebrity endorsement would create excitement in the foreign markets.

At last the discussion came to an end, and Nic politely excused himself, knowing he didn't have much time if he wanted to make it home to take the conference call with his father.

Yet after reaching his car, he realized he'd left his cell phone behind. With a soft oath, Nic returned to the building and crossed the cool, dark lobby, pungent with the smell of oak, sulfur and fermenting grapes. When he was a boy he'd thought the smell too sour and raw. Now it was comforting. Like coming home.

Opening the door to the wine-tasting room, Niccolo heard Maggie's name mentioned. He froze, sure he'd been mistaken. But the vintner at the far end of the table repeated himself.

"That's right. I saw her myself. Maggie Buckner is back, and from what I heard, she's in some serious trouble."

CHAPTER THREE

NICCOLO froze, his hand on the doorknob. Maggie, his Maggie, in trouble? No, he hadn't heard right. Maggie was doing just fine.

"That poor family!" Another grower spoke. "They've certainly had their share of trouble. The last thing John and Eileen need is more heartache."

Niccolo felt rooted to the spot. He knew he should open the door and interrupt. He knew he should intervene. But he couldn't move. Couldn't bring himself to speak.

"They said she wasn't drinking," a woman said. "They tested her at the police station."

"But that doesn't mean she wasn't driving recklessly," one of the men interrupted. "I don't know another teenager that pierced more body parts than Maggie Buckner."

"It was just her ears. She had a whole row of studs up and down her ear."

The gossip infuriated Niccolo. He knew people in small towns liked to talk, but this was ridiculous. He opened the door and stepped into the room, but no one saw him. They were too busy wagging their tongues.

"Why didn't her parents do something?" the vintner from Copper Cellars demanded. "I'll tell you why. They couldn't. Maggie had John and Eileen over a barrel. If Maggie's in trouble, she has no one to blame but herself. If she cared about anyone but herself Jared would be alive today—''

''That's enough!'' Niccolo's voice sliced through the room. ''It's been years since the accident. Why can't you leave her alone?''

The growers gazed at him, white-faced and uncomfortable.

A moment ago voices had filled the tasting room. Now silence lay like a suffocating blanket. Finally, one of the growers spoke. ''Niccolo, it was just talk. No harm was meant.''

''I'm tired of this. I'm tired of you using Maggie as a topic for discussion.''

''Don't be mad, Nic—''

''I'm not mad, I'm furious. You've never cared a whit about Maggie other than labeling her difficult and a troublemaker.'' His voice rang in the hushed room. ''By the way, Maggie *is* in town. She's my guest. She's staying at my house while she works with the Hunts on their garden renovation.''

His chest tightened, his anger turning on himself. This was his fault. They blamed Maggie because they didn't know the truth. He should have spoken up years ago, put the matter straight. Instead he'd bitten his tongue and looked the other way. ''And one last thing,'' he added, his voice throbbing with emotion. ''Maggie's not in trouble. If she was in trouble, I'd be the first to know.''

The sun was setting when Meg pulled into the Dominici driveway. The ten-hour workdays were putting a strain on her nerves. Today her headache threatened to reduce her to tears. She desperately craved rest and a quiet, dark room.

Francesca met her at the door. She anxiously knotted her apron. "Niccolo is waiting for you by the pool."

"I'm not interested in a swim."

The housekeeper's forehead furrowed. "I don't think he's thinking of a swim, either."

Meg heard the warning in Francesca's voice. "Has something happened?"

"I've told him nothing."

"Francesca—"

"He returned from a winery meeting in a black mood."

"What happened?"

"I don't know, but I warn you, something's eating at him."

Meg sighed, already exhausted. She wasn't prepared for a scene with Nic. He was the strongest, most stubborn man she'd ever met. If he had a bone to pick, he picked it clean. She stepped out of the villa's cool interior onto the broad steps leading to the pool. The setting sun cast long red-gold rays across the water's surface, reflecting onto the sweeping stone deck and illuminating the massive Italian clay pots filled with dwarf citrus trees. The heady perfume of lemon blossoms hung in the air, a favorite fragrance of Meg's since she had been a girl. But it was impossible to enjoy the scent now, not with her anxiety about Niccolo's mood.

She spotted a towel stretched across one of the chaise longues, but she didn't see Nic.

Relief briefly washed over her. He must have returned to the house for something.

Her shoulders dropped, and she took a deep breath.

What on earth had happened at the winery meeting? How could it involve her?

Slowly Meg walked along the edge of the pool. The garden had always enchanted her. She responded to the luxurious use of blue tile and stone, the garden a fanciful interpretation of life in ancient Rome. More massive pots, clinging vines, small citrus trees. The enclosed garden was a perfect balance of light and scent and sound.

"I thought you trusted me."

Meg started, surprised by the grate of Nic's deep voice. She turned toward the sound, a small shiver coursing down her spine. She shouldn't let him unnerve her. He couldn't do anything to her. They were adults. Equals.

Nic sat beneath a market umbrella, his face hidden in the shade. "You should have come to me if you needed help." Disappointment tinged his voice.

"I don't need help," she answered sharply, defensive.

He pushed up from the chair and walked toward her. His casual shirt hung open, unbuttoned to reveal his bronzed chest and the hard, flat muscles in his abdomen.

Meg inhaled quickly, taken aback by his blatant virility. He'd never been shy, but he'd never been so confident, either.

"I hate hearing others talk about you."

She felt a lump form in her chest. It threatened to seal her throat.

He glanced at her as he walked past her. "Because they do talk, Maggie. They enjoy your escapades."

"I don't know what you're talking about."

"No?"

"No." She barely managed to get the word out, her voice strangled, her chest tight like a vise. He couldn't know. He couldn't have found out.

But he would, sooner or later.

The intensity in his golden eyes held her captive. She swallowed hard, lifted her chin. "Is there a point to this, Nic? I'm not in the mood for games."

"And I've never played games, *cara*."

She bristled at his tone. He made her feel sixteen again, and it was all she could do to keep from rolling her eyes. "So what do you want?"

Niccolo smoothed the towel on the chaise longue. "I want you to sit down here—" he patted the chaise "—and tell me what you're trying so hard to hide."

"I'm not trying to hide anything."

"Lie number one."

"Nic!"

"I'll ask you again. What are you trying to hide?"

"Nothing. I'm here to do a job. I'm doing the job. That's it."

"I don't believe you."

He wanted to fight. He was trying to be insulting. For a split second she considered telling him the truth. It would shut him up. Stun him to silence. Because of course Nic would be furious. She would have committed the ultimate sin.

But she wouldn't tell him. It wasn't his problem. She refused to let him interfere. "I'm going back to the house. I don't have to put up with this."

His expression changed, his fierce features softening. "*Cara*, I don't want to quarrel. Why can't you sit down and let us talk? You once told me everything."

"I was naive."

"We were friends."

"Friends don't judge each other."

"Who said I'm judging you?"

"You will."

"So you do have a problem." His eyes gleamed, then he smiled triumphantly.

It was a game to him. He didn't care about her. Didn't care about her feelings. He just wanted to be right. So typical. "That's charming, Nic."

His eyebrows met in the middle. Fine lines were etched on either side of his mouth. He was clearly losing patience. "Maggie, sit."

"As enticing as that sounds, I'll pass."

"Why?"

"Because I am not a dog and I do not respond to doggie commands."

"Doggie commands?"

"Sit. Stay. Roll over." She crossed her arms, glaring at him. "For a man with an excellent command of seven languages, your communication skills are hopeless."

He looked equally irritated. "I do not speak this way to everyone, just to unreasonable girls who do not listen."

"Ah, that's where you've made your first mistake. I am not a girl. I'm twenty-eight. Which leads me to your second mistake. Despite your medieval upbringing, women do not have to listen to you."

"That's illogical."

"Just like I'm unreasonable."

"Yes!" he said, his voice like thunder. "You're impossible. You drive me to distraction."

A breeze rustled the leaves of the trees, freeing a curl from her ponytail. Her chest burned, aching with bottled-up emotion. "Then leave me alone. I'm not who you want me to be. I'm not who you think I am."

He closed the distance between them and took her by the upper arms. "That's not true. You're my Maggie."

"I'm not. I'm not your anything."

The expression in his golden eyes was pure pain. He held her so firmly that it felt as if his fingers would sink into her very bones. "Don't say that," he rasped. "I've lost Jared. I won't lose you, too."

A current of electricity surged through her, and Niccolo's eyes narrowed, his gaze dropping to her mouth. Her lower lip quivered as if he'd run the tip of his finger across the sensitive skin and Meg pulled back, terrified. *He meant to kiss her!* No. She couldn't let this happen.

His dark head dropped, blotting the last lingering rays of sun. Dragging her closer against him, he let her feel the hard, taut length of him. "I will not lose you," he muttered thickly against her lips. "I swear it, Maggie."

Then his mouth covered hers, hard and fast, expressing possession.

She closed her eyes, a shiver coursing down her spine. He smelled of oak and citrus, red wine and sunlight. As his lips parted hers, her knees went weak. He tasted even better. His lips, tongue, caressed hers. His warmth penetrated her bones, melting her into him.

She wanted to resist, but couldn't. It was exactly as she feared. She wanted him, oh, she still wanted him!

The kiss deepened, and his hands gentled, sliding up her arms to cradle the back of her head. She shivered against him and felt his body harden, making her aware of his desire. Just as suddenly his head lifted and he stared into her eyes.

Breathlessly she gazed at him, hope and desire filling her heart. But just as quickly as he'd drawn her to him, he thrust her away, the warmth in his golden eyes fading, the light gold flecks hardening, the passion dying.

He realized what he had done. He regretted the kiss. He hadn't meant to kiss her. It had been an accident, an error of judgment. Which should have made her happy. Niccolo had always held himself up as a model of decorum. Now he'd proved himself just as human as she was. They were even. A kiss for a kiss. Mistake for a mistake. Equals.

Stupid tears burned at the back of her eyes, but she covered her chaotic emotions with a quick laugh. "Trying to teach me a lesson, aren't you? Well, Nic, that's one way to silence the critics."

His jaw tightened, and he swallowed. It took him longer to recover his composure. "I didn't intend to do that. I was just trying to make a statement—"

"Oh, you did. No one has ever tried to kiss me into submission before."

"I'm quite serious. I'm trying to do the right thing."

"Which is what you've always tried to do." She managed a small, tight smile yet her heart continued to race and her legs felt unsteady, her body still traitorously warm from the kiss. She forced her chin up and a note of bravado into her shaking voice. "But there are some things you can't fix, and there are some people you can't change."

"I don't understand."

Her resolve was cracking. She could hear it inside her head as clearly as if it were an iceberg roaring as it broke in two. "No, you don't want to understand. There's a difference!" she retorted, worn out from sparring and overwhelmed by his kiss.

If he was determined to know the truth, she'd tell him. It wasn't as if she'd be able to hide the facts much longer. She was beginning to show, and soon everyone would know what she'd been trying to keep secret. "Nic, I'm pregnant. I'm expecting a baby early next year."

She didn't think Niccolo could look more shocked or more disappointed.

"Do your parents know?"

Of course that would be his first question.

Respectability, accountability, social conventions. These were always his first concerns. She wished he didn't care so much about what people thought. It was what was in people's hearts that mattered most.

"I've told my mother," she answered after a brief silence. "I plan to tell Dad when they return from the trip."

"You didn't want to ruin his vacation."

"I know he'd worry."

Niccolo shook his head once, expressing disbelief. "You don't think your mother is worried?"

This was the hard part. Meg knew she didn't have to answer to Nic, but she also knew Nic wouldn't leave the subject alone. It was better to get the truth out. Get it over and done with. "Mom thinks she's coming home to a wedding."

Nic could say more with his eyes and jaw than anyone else. His jaw tightened, the tiny muscle popping, accenting the hard angle of bone and golden skin. "There's no wedding?"

"No."

He stared at her through narrowed eyes, his black lashes fanning his high, bronzed cheekbones. His hard expression didn't change. The only sign he gave of his mounting fury was the pulse beating at the base of his throat. She stared at the tiny rapid pulse, fascinated. He was upset, very upset.

"Why isn't there a wedding?" He bit out the brutally short syllables.

"Because."

His head jerked, his gaze leaping to hers. "Because?"

Her nerves screamed, the tension so tight she felt as if her muscles had been pulled on a string, turning her into a dangling puppet. She shook her head, her voice failing her. He wouldn't understand. No matter what she said, no matter what she told him, Niccolo would not understand.

His fierce golden gaze bored straight through her. "Where's the baby's father?"

"The baby doesn't have a father."

"Don't tell me. It was a miraculous conception."

His sarcasm stung. She felt herself flush, overwhelmed by an onslaught of emotion. "I'm not the first woman to have a baby on her own."

"No, and you probably won't be the last. But there's no glory in being an unwed mother."

"There's no shame in it, either."

"No?" One of his black eyebrows lifted. His softly spoken word hung between them, mocking her.

Again he was reminding her of the past, pulling

her skeletons from the closet and shaking them in her face. He had a memory like an elephant, and he'd never let her forget her many mistakes, like the six-inch-high platform shoes she wore the summer she turned sixteen, the lime-green streak she put in her hair one Sunday morning when her parents were at church, the night she hot-wired a neighbor's work truck and went for a joyride that took out the rear end of the truck and put five stitches in her temple near her hairline.

Meg clenched her hands into fists, fighting desperately to hang on to her pride. "The baby might be an accident, but I'll be a good mother."

Niccolo shook his head again and walked to the table. He lifted one of the crystal decanters and poured himself a drink.

She waited for him to say something, but he didn't speak. He merely swirled the amber liquid in his crystal tumbler and stared across the patio toward the pool. The sun glimmered on the water, reflecting the sky and scattered clouds.

"I want this baby," she said quietly.

"Just like you want everything," he retorted before lifting his glass and taking a swallow.

She felt as if he'd slapped her. Her heart dropped. Her mouth went dry. "What does that mean?"

He tapped a finger against the crystal, making the tumbler ring. "It means you're still just a little girl, unwilling to accept responsibility for your mistakes."

"Who are you to pass judgment? You're no paragon of virtue, Niccolo. You've had lovers since you were seventeen, some of them twice your age."

"It's different."

"How so?"

"There are different standards for men and women, *cara*. Surely, even you know that."

"You're medieval."

"I'm telling the truth." He took another sip from his glass. "If you don't love him enough to marry him, what were you doing sleeping with him?"

"It's none of your business."

He slowly, deliberately set the glass down before turning to face her. His expression was grim, his golden eyes dark, intense. "It is now."

How could she be pregnant?

No, he knew how, that much was obvious—his jaw tightened angrily—but how could she have been so careless? If she was going to sleep around, she should have been prepared. Sex without protection wasn't just irresponsible, it was dangerous.

Although it was well past midnight, Niccolo poured himself a second cup of espresso and sat at his desk with his reports on the new Merlot. The vats were tested at regular intervals to measure acidity during the fermenting process, and this year's Merlot was proving to be especially temperamental. But the percentages and graphs might as well have been written in invisible ink. Niccolo stared at the sheets of paper and saw nothing.

Nothing, that is, but Maggie.

He was so disappointed in her that he couldn't think straight. Maggie, pregnant.

Her father, a salt-of-the-earth man, would be extremely unhappy about the news. Decent, hardworking, plain speaking, John was well respected by valley growers and ranchers. Everyone knew how close he'd been to his only son, just as everyone knew that John Buckner didn't have much patience with his rebellious daughter.

As a teenager, Nic had heard John Buckner say more than once that Maggie was a disaster waiting to happen. John didn't dislike his only daughter. He just didn't understand her.

Later, as Jared approached college age, he confided in Niccolo that he dreaded heading to college and leaving Maggie at home alone. He'd tried to be a buffer between his father and Maggie. Jared hated to make waves. Maggie was a veritable storm.

A storm was right. And John Buckner was going to be livid about the baby.

Nic pushed the paperwork across his desk, unable to concentrate. He shouldn't worry about Maggie. It wasn't his place to save her skin. But someone had to care enough about Maggie to intervene. Ever since Jared's death her parents had seemed too grief-stricken and overwhelmed to try. Her teachers hadn't had the time nor the inclination. People in town had just gossiped. That left him.

If he'd had more courage a long time ago Maggie might have suffered less. He shouldn't have allowed her to restage the accident scene, shouldn't have let her accept all the blame. Maybe if he'd been stronger then, Maggie and her parents would have a different relationship today.

Perhaps he and Maggie would be different people today.

Rubbing his closed eyes, Nic resisted remembering the accident. That Christmas Eve had become such a terrible memory that he shied away from recalling the details. Instead he'd begun to deny the truth, allowing him to bury the pain.

But Maggie hadn't been at fault that night. Jared had been at the wheel. Jared had been drinking.

And so had he.

Niccolo opened his eyes and gazed across the room, noting the plaques and honorable mentions his wines had won at international expositions. As a winemaker he was a success. But as a man?

Nic abruptly pushed away from the desk and stood.

He couldn't change the past, but maybe he could set the record straight. He'd tell Maggie's parents the truth about the accident, and maybe Maggie would finally have a chance to develop a real relationship with her father.

Meg dashed out the front door and down the villa's flagstone steps before Francesca spotted her. She would not let herself get detained this morning. Breakfast with Niccolo was about as relaxing as running with the bulls.

Keys jingling, she hastily unlocked the rental car's door. With a toss, she sent her briefcase sailing onto the passenger seat, and she slid behind the steering wheel as if sprinting in a race. Reaching for the door, Meg suddenly discovered she couldn't close it.

"Like a thief in the night," Niccolo taunted.

Meg's heart nearly leaped from her chest, and she jumped, scared to death. "What?"

He held the door firmly, knowing she'd be unable to close it. A cool smile tilted the corners of his lips. "Sneaking away, *cara*?"

Something in his silken voice made her stomach

plummet. The fine hairs on the nape of her neck rose, her skin prickling with keen awareness. He hadn't even touched her and yet her body quivered from head to toe. "I have to go. I'm late."

"It's not even seven yet."

"I know, but I have so much to do. I must get to work right away."

"Lie after lie," he drawled, cocking his head to better study her. "You've become quite an accomplished storyteller."

"Be quiet, Nic," she snapped. "This is getting awfully tedious." Impatiently, Meg turned the key in the ignition, starting the car. Thankfully the engine vroomed with impressive noise. She had to raise her voice to be heard above the roar. "Now please step away before you get hurt."

"Hurt? Now there's a thought. Run Nic over. Exciting headlines for tomorrow's paper."

"Good grief! Can't you let me go?"

"No." He leaned inside the car, his face inches from hers. "And as much as I enjoy listening to you gun the engine, I think you're better off inside, eating breakfast. You can't afford to skip meals. It's not fair to the baby."

"The baby will get something downtown. The baby likes deli food."

"Francesca already laid a place for you at the breakfast table."

Meg's foot worked the accelerator. She deliberately gunned the motor a couple more times. "What was that? What did you say? I can't hear you!"

Nic's lips flattened over his teeth, and his black hair fell forward across his strong brow. He looked distinctly tyrannical. A fierce Italian nobleman from

the fifteenth century. He didn't care about rules.
Didn't give a damn for polite conversation.

"Don't push me."

"Don't you push me!" she contradicted.

Grimly he reached over her, his forearm brushing
her breasts, and grabbed for the keys.

Fear, pure instinctive fear, rocketed through Meg.
The only thing she could think about was saving herself. Niccolo was furious and he'd give her hell. No
way was she going to stick around listen to another
of his righteous tirades.

Adrenaline flooding her veins, she slapped at his
hand, her palm smacking him so hard that hers stung
and drew sharp tears to her eyes.

Niccolo pulled back, stunned. "You little—"

Meg didn't need to hear the rest. His thundering
voice told her all she needed to know. With split-
second timing she slammed the car door closed,
locked it from the inside and shifted into drive.

Her hands shook as she rolled down the window
a half inch. "Sorry, Nic," she shouted. "I'd love to
talk but I just don't have the time right now. See you
tonight!"

CHAPTER FOUR

IF SHE thought she'd gotten away with something, her brief flirtation with freedom ended at noon when Niccolo showed up at the Hunts. He drew the elderly couple aside and spoke with them quietly for a moment. Before Meg could act, Niccolo was escorting her from the house to his red convertible sports car, his fingers viselike on her arm near her elbow.

Niccolo's classic 1962 Ferrari Spider roadster roared down the deserted road toward the highway. Meg sat rigidly on the supple leather seat, too furious to speak. How dare he show up at her job and collect her as if she were a child at school!

Niccolo shot her an amused look. "Breathe. You're starting to turn blue."

"Don't talk to me!"

"I'm doing this for your own good."

She clutched her notebook in her lap, resisting the urge to toss it at his head. "You had no right," she complained. "We were in the middle of an intensive discussion."

Nic shifted, driving swiftly through northern California's rolling hills. The golden landscape whirled past the convertible like the backdrop on an old movie set. "Sorry."

Sorry? That's all he could say? He'd broken off an important discussion, hauled her to the car and drove the back roads faster than a racing driver. Sorry definitely wouldn't cut it.

He cast a sidelong glance at her. "You should wear white more often. It suits you."

Now he was going for the charm. Anything to disarm her. "It's winter white," she retorted coolly, catching a glimpse of her cashmere suit jacket and navy trousers. She wore everything long and loose these days, wanting comfort instead of style as her waist began to expand.

"Anyway, it looks good on you. Perhaps it's the color in your cheeks today. Your face glows."

With anger. Meg caught a tendril of her hair as it whipped in her face. "Can you put up the top, please?"

"But it's lovely out, *cara*. Relax. Enjoy the sun."

"I'm not on vacation," she answered sharply, her chest rising and falling with quick, short breaths. She struggled to put her anger into coherent sentences. "Turn around and take me back."

"Take you back?"

"Now. *Please.*"

"I'm sorry. I've made plans for us. I thought we needed some time together—" his golden gaze raked her "—some time alone."

Time together? Time alone? It was the last thing she needed. Time with Nic was like time in a torture chamber. Each conversation felt as if it took place on a bed of nails. "Nic, I was working. You can't just show up and drag me away."

"But I did."

"That's not the point. This—my life—it isn't an episode of 'The Flintstones.'"

He sighed and shook his head. "How tragic. If you were raised in Italy, you would have a knowledge of music and art instead of cartoons."

Meg slapped one hand against her head in mock horror. "Yes, go right ahead, make fun of American education. Mock my lowbrow culture. Cartoons instead of opera. Video games in place of books. Hamburgers and fries rather than haute cuisine. Isn't that right?"

His smile was lazy enjoyment. "Yes, *cara*, that about sums it up."

She caught the twitch of his lip and realized he'd enjoyed baiting her. This was his way of getting back at her for driving away from him this morning.

Meg settled herself more comfortably in the roadster's seat. She glanced at Nic's profile, noting the fine lines fanning from the corners of his eyes and the grooves along his mouth. He looked older, more handsome than he did at twenty-two. Maturity suited him. Somehow she sensed he'd be even better looking at fifty.

Her anger melted. It was impossible to stay mad at Nic. But then he knew that. When they were younger he'd say something to hurt her feelings but then he'd smile, tease her, and she'd end up forgiving him.

She plucked another curl from her cheek and tucked it behind her ear. "So what did you tell the Hunts?"

He shrugged and shifted down, taking a tight corner. "I told them an emergency came up." He cast her a sidelong glance. "Personal matter, a family thing."

"Nic, the Hunts are my biggest, most important clients. I can't afford to lose them."

"Don't worry. Your big, important client will not fire you. I hosted their big fund-raiser at the winery last year. The Hunts raised a quarter of a million dollars that night. The Hunts—" he drawled their name for emphasis, his golden eyes mocking "—are still indebted to me."

She didn't know whether to be irritated or amused. No matter what he did, Niccolo came out smelling like a rose. She turned slightly, looking at the rolling hills. "Where are we going, anyway?"

"To the coast. I thought we could get a bite of dinner. Talk without interruption."

Torture without interruption. More of his inquisition. "I'd rather work," she answered dryly.

"I'm sure you would," he answered. "You were quite anxious to go this morning."

She felt her lips twitch, a bubble of laughter forming inside her. "Mm," she murmured, trying to keep from laughing.

"You slapped me," he added.

"Your hand."

"You slapped my hand."

Her cheeks ached with the effort to not laugh. Her eyes began to burn. She felt them start to water. "It was a gentle slap."

"My hand was red for nearly an hour."

"You must have sensitive skin."

"Fine. Next time I'll haul you over my knee and give you a not-so-gentle slap on your bottom. We'll see who has sensitive skin then."

Meg suddenly lost the urge to laugh. Her heart skipped a beat. "You wouldn't."

He cast a sardonic look in her direction, daring her to provoke him. "Try me," he murmured with evil intent in his warm golden eyes. When she didn't answer, he chuckled quietly. "Don't look so shocked. It wouldn't be the first time you were spanked."

"Yes, but that was by my *father*," she answered, mortified. She could feel the blood rush to her cheeks, her face burning. "I'd never let a man spank me."

"Oh, come, Maggie, you can't be such a prude. You're a woman of the world. You must have indulged in your share of erotic games."

"Spanking is not an erotic game."

"Oh?" His soft laughter taunted her again. "I suppose it depends on who is doing the spanking."

She had a vision of herself over Nic's lap, her bottom up, exposed to the air, and she shuddered. It would be humiliating and horrible, and she'd never let it happen, never in a million years. Yet the insides of her thighs trembled and her lower belly clenched, as if anticipating the torture and the pleasure.

Niccolo would be a practiced lover. Of that she was sure.

"I'd like to change the subject," she announced frostily, as if to deny the heat in her limbs and the warmth spreading at the apex of her thighs. She couldn't want him, couldn't desire him. She'd thrown herself at him once and she'd never make the same mistake again.

His golden gaze assessed her, lingering on her mouth and the heightened color in her face. "Of course, *cara*. This conversation is too tame. Love, sex, erotica…it's all rather dull. Why don't we talk about gardens instead?"

"Very funny."

"I'm sure you have an opinion on the ideal height

for a mature hedge. Or tell me, what is the perfect perennial for a garden in the wine country?''

''Save the sarcasm. Just turn the car around. I want to go home.''

''Home. Is the villa home?''

''You know what I mean.''

''No, I don't know what you mean. I don't even know who you are anymore, *cara*. You're pregnant, alone, fabricating lies to your mother about make-believe weddings so she won't worry.'' He reached out and ejected a CD from the car stereo. ''Maggie, would you please select another CD?''

How could he switch gears like that? Ridicule her and then ask for a new music selection? ''I don't want music,'' she answered, ''I just want to return to work.''

''There's a disk there, in the console. Could you please hand it to me?''

She did as he asked then turned to look out the window. Pressing her palm against her mouth, she fought to hold back a stream of insults. He was impossible. He wasn't listening to a thing she said. Obviously, he didn't care.

They were heading west, and the open golden hills were giving way to scattered groves of oak, scrub brush and pine. She fidgeted in her seat, crossing her arms only to uncross them again.

''Maggie, I've come to a decision.''

His serious tone made her sit up a little straighter. All hint of laughter was gone from his voice. Glancing at him, she noted his dark, brooding expression. ''About what?''

''About a mistake I made years ago.'' He looked

at her sharply, glints flashing in his golden eyes. "About that Christmas Eve."

It was all he needed to say. Ever since Jared died, it was the way they referred to the accident. *That Christmas Eve.*

Butterflies tumbled in her stomach. Frightened, she waited in silence for him to continue.

"The way I behaved that night, and since then, it's reprehensible. I allowed you to take the blame—"

"I insisted."

"I was older. A man." He shook his head once, his mouth twisting bitterly. "I was wrong, and it's time for me to set the record straight."

"No."

"It was his accident, Maggie, not yours."

"I don't know what you're talking about."

"You know exactly what I'm talking about."

"I was driving. I was goofing off. I crashed into the tree."

"Jared was driving. I was in the passenger seat. You were in the back seat." It sounded as if he was spitting glass, each word, each vowel short and sharp, cutting straight through her heart.

"I don't remember."

"Cut it out. You know exactly what I'm talking about, but in all these years we've never discussed that night, never discussed your decision or my stupidity in letting you switch places with Jared."

"He was my brother!"

"And my best friend, but that doesn't mean he was perfect. Maggie, your parents—"

"If you tell them, Nic, I'll never speak to you again."

"When you leave here Friday you probably won't speak to me again, so where's the danger?"

His sarcasm made blood surge to her face. He sounded so cold, so determined. Panic gripped her. Nic couldn't do this. He couldn't break his vow. He'd promised years ago to stick with her story. He'd agreed that her parents would be devastated if they'd known Jared had been drinking.

"My dad idolizes Jared," she said, her voice small and faint. "Jared's memory is precious to him. If you tell them, you'll destroy my father's memory of him."

"But what about you, Maggie? What about *your* relationship with your father?"

"It's fine. We talk once every two weeks. I call on Sunday, he tells me about the ranch, I tell him about my work, we say we love each other and then we hang up."

"Maggie, he thinks you killed Jared."

It felt as if Nic was scratching his nails down a chalkboard. The skin on her spine crawled. Her stomach cramped hard. "He's forgiven me," she whispered.

"What I did was wrong. I let your parents blame you. I let the entire town blame you. It was a selfish, cowardly thing for me to do."

"I begged you."

She saw the muscle pop in his jaw, saw the anger and self-loathing flare in his eyes. "Jared would never have let you shoulder the blame. Jared would have fought tooth and nail to protect you."

Her shoulders hunched. She tried to block the sound of Nic's voice. This conversation was excruciating. She couldn't believe that she and Nic were having it in the first place. "It was Christmas Eve," she whispered, "he was just having fun."

"Yes, it was Christmas Eve. We were having a great time being together again. Jared was in fine form, too, joking and laughing and telling us stories about his year away at school. But Jared had been drinking. I'd been drinking, too."

Niccolo looked at her, sorrow darkening his eyes. "Maggie, I failed you and I failed Jared—"

"That's not true. You did what I asked you to do. I have no regrets. It was horrible that he..." She drew a rough breath. "Died. Why make it worse for Mom and Dad? Jared was the oldest. He was the ideal son. Eagle Scout. Student body president. Straight A student."

She reached up and wiped the dampness from her eyes. "Heck, he even saved a drowning kid one summer when he was fifteen." Her voice quavered and she wiped another tear. "The river was flooding, remember that summer? And that boy couldn't get out. So Jared jumped in. He didn't think twice. He just jumped in and pulled the boy out."

She looked at Nic with tears in her eyes. "He was a hero, Nic. He was my hero. I couldn't let everything good he did die with him."

They stopped for a late afternoon coffee in Bodega Bay. "You'll have decaffeinated, of course," Nic reminded her as the waitress approached.

Things had been unusually strained between them since Nic had brought up the accident and Jared's death. Nic had dropped the subject and they'd lapsed into silence.

Now they were seated at a small table overlooking

the rugged coastline. The picture window revealed wispy blue sky and an endless expanse of water.

Meg hadn't planned on ordering coffee, but Nic's authoritative tone made her want a cup. "The latest research says that small amounts of caffeine won't hurt the baby."

"You already had a cup at breakfast. You don't need another." He scanned the small menu before suggesting she try the fruit juices or one of the blended frozen yogurt drinks.

How like Nic. He relished his power and wielded authority like a barbarian nobleman. "Sorry," she said lightly, knowing her glibness would irritate him. "I'm not a smoothie aficionado."

"Fine. Order milk." He snapped the menu shut and looked at the waitress. "I'll have an espresso."

Meg smiled at the waitress. "A cup of coffee, please."

"Decaf," he added firmly. He gave her a hard look. "And she'll have the half sandwich and salad combination."

The waitress glanced at Meg before looking at Nic. "Would she like tomatoes and sprouts on her sandwich?"

"No sprouts. Tomatoes and lettuce."

The waitress, with a puzzled glance, departed. Meg stared at Nic, incredulous. "You can't order for me," she said.

"But I just did." He shrugged and unfolded his napkin, incredibly graceful for a man of his power and size. "You need to eat. The baby needs you to eat. You're far too thin."

"Niccolo, this is not your baby."

"Obviously. If I'd got you pregnant, I'd remember."

Heaven help her, what a thing to say! She clenched her knees together, feeling dreadfully exposed.

"And then," he continued, leaning forward on his elbows, stretching his shirt taut across his broad shoulders, "I'd drag you to the nearest priest and make you take my name and make you wear my ring."

More heat surged through her middle, stirring her senses. She resisted the coiling of desire, unwilling to contemplate marrying Nic. "Ah, lovely. A moral de' Medici!"

He smiled faintly but there was no humor in his eyes. "Why didn't you use protection?"

She felt herself blush, the heat surging through her cheeks. "That's a rather personal question."

"I want to know."

"Nic—"

"Were you so swept away by the moment that it slipped your mind? Or do you practice unsafe sex—"

"No!" Her fierce denial silenced him. Breathing hard, she struggled to gain control of her chaotic emotions. Nic had a way of getting under her skin. "I don't—didn't…" She shook her head, miserably aware of her stupidity. "There was a problem with the…condom."

The look he gave her was one of incredulity. "I've never had a problem with a condom in my life."

From the heat in her cheeks, she knew she was turning bright pink. This was far more than she needed to know about Nic's sex life.

"I wasn't the one wearing the condom, Nic," she

retorted, humiliated by his look and tone. "I didn't realize there was a problem."

Nic grunted and leaned back, drumming his fingers on the tabletop. "Fool."

"What?"

"Your friend—"

"Mark."

"Mark was a fool." Nic's brow creased with fury. "A real man takes the time to make sure protection *works*." He must have noticed her disbelieving look. "Maggie, this area we're talking about, it's quite sensitive."

She felt flushed from head to toe. She reached for her glass of ice water and took a gulp.

But Nic wasn't finished. "A condom isn't rocket science. A man knows when something isn't right."

"Okay." She swirled her glass, spinning the ice in the chilly water. "Got it. Thanks for the biology lesson, Nic."

To her surprise he began to laugh. The warmth in his voice drew delicate shivers across her skin. "You're laughing," she accused him, looking up and meeting his gaze.

"I have to, Maggie. I've never met anyone like you."

"That's a compliment, I'm sure," she retorted, glimpsing the waitress heading their way.

Meg made room in front of her for the salad and sandwich. Suddenly she felt ravenous. Her mouth watered as she glimpsed the moist turkey and avocado sandwich.

She'd never tell Nic, but sometimes she did think he knew exactly what she needed.

CHAPTER FIVE

"TELL me about the baby's father," Nic said, unexpectedly as they walked along the sandy shore after leaving the restaurant. A crisp breeze blew, and the waves churned, short and choppy, white foamy crests forming on each wave.

They hadn't gone a hundred yards down the beach, and already Nic was at it again. "No."

"Why not?"

She couldn't help laughing. Niccolo didn't give up. She'd never met anyone so persistent in her life. "Because it's pointless," she answered with a brief shake of her head. "There's nothing you need to know."

He bent and picked up a smooth piece of driftwood, the breeze catching his linen shirt, billowing the olive green fabric like a sail. "Humor me."

Humor him. That's all she'd been doing since arriving in Healdsburg.

He must have noticed the wry twist of her lips because he chuckled softly and with a swift fling of his arm, Nic tossed the driftwood to sea, the weathered piece flying high until it came splashing down.

Meg glanced at him from beneath lowered lashes. His hard, chiseled features appeared more relaxed. Creases fanned from his eyes, but these were faint smile lines, not lines of anger.

She still found it hard to believe she'd thought Mark resembled Nic. Maybe Mark was dark, and handsome in a smooth, nonoffensive kind of way, but he could never rival Nic's strength, nor his formidable power.

"What would you like to know?" she asked, hoping her tone sounded suitably casual.

"What does he do, to start with?"

She didn't think it would hurt to disclose Mark's occupation. It wasn't as if Niccolo could track Mark down based on a first name and a profession. "He's an investment banker in New York."

"I take it he's successful?"

"He's doing all right for himself."

"Attractive?"

If you like tall, dark and handsome. Meg squirmed inwardly. "He's not bad."

"A ringing endorsement."

"Nic, what do you want me to say? The condom slipped because the sex was so great?"

Nic glanced at her, eyebrows rising. "Was the sex great?"

"No!" The admission slipped out before she could help herself. Blood surged to her face. She felt utterly foolish. What a ridiculous thing to confess, and to Nic, of all people!

Covering her tracks, she hastily added. "I mean, it was fine. Perfectly fine—"

"Perfectly fine?" he interrupted, his gaze riveted on her. She wasn't sure if she heard incredulity or revulsion in his voice. "That's the best you can say? This man, your *lover*, got you pregnant. I'd hope for a little better than fine, *cara*."

"Oh, come on, Nic. Be realistic. Not everyone has great sex. Some people click. Some people don't. And some people..." She drew a deep breath, wondering how on earth he'd gotten her to say this much. "Some people have so little chemistry they shouldn't even dream of being together."

"That's not why you and Mark aren't together, is it?" Nic's frown deepened, his tone severe. "Maggie, surely you're not throwing away a relationship because it lacks chemistry?"

Throwing away a relationship? She almost laughed. There never had been a relationship. Just her misguided notions about men and romance and sex.

"Nic, you should see yourself. You look exactly like Miss Herrington when she was scolding the class for not completing the five-paragraph essay on time."

"Wasn't she the teacher who kicked you out of class?"

"I didn't put the stink bomb in her desk. That was Charles. But she didn't believe me."

"Maggie, we're not talking about Miss Herrington. We're talking about Mark."

Which was exactly what she didn't want to discuss. Nic and Mark were light-years apart. Two different breeds of men. No matter how many questions Nic asked, he'd never understand about Mark, and he'd never understand what Maggie saw in Mark in the first place.

"But I didn't give Charles the stink bomb, either," she answered as if he'd never spoken, desperately trying to divert his attention. "You know, Nic, that's all hearsay."

"You're incorrigible, Maggie Buckner. I'm trying to have a serious conversation with you and you can't even give me a straight answer." He caught her amazed expression. "What? You didn't think I'd know you were trying to sidetrack me?"

"No, I can't believe you know a word like incorrigible in English. I don't even know the word in English."

"Maggie."

She heard the indulgence in his voice as he said her name and felt a small thrill course through her. She shouldn't care what Nic thought of her and yet, perversely, she did. He was the one person whose good opinion mattered.

And whether she liked it or not, she still desperately wanted him to think well of her. Nic wasn't just part of her past. Her feelings for him were more intense than ever. She longed to have someone agree with her, someone support her decision. If only Nic could be on her side!

He reached out, caught her hand in his and drew it to his mouth. Pressing a small kiss to the back of her fingers he said, "Surely, Maggie, you know that passion is fleeting. Real relationships are based on friendship and trust. Don't let this chemistry be the obstacle preventing you from marrying Mark. Think of the baby, Maggie. Think of being a family."

His lips sent delicious shivers up and down her spine. She touched the tip of her tongue to her upper lip, wondering how on earth she could still be so attracted to him. He made her want things no man had ever made her want. He made her crave more warmth, more touch, more skin.

"This…it's not—" She broke off, finding it difficult to think. Niccolo's mouth was so warm against her fingers, his lips making her skin feel like velvet. She pulled free of him, jamming her hand behind her

back as if she was putting out a fire. She had to keep
Nic at arm's length. She couldn't let him keep touching her, melting her reserve, warming her body so
that she hummed with need.

"It's not a chemistry thing," she answered indignantly, her voice quavering faintly as blood drummed
in her ears. "I'm not that shallow."

No? she mocked herself. *You're standing here
aching for Nic to take you in his arms again, aching
for him to kiss you senseless. You don't even need
an excuse to forget your pride!*

"So what is it?" He turned her to face him, his
hands on her shoulders, his palms flexed against her
skin. Slowly his thumbs caressed her collarbone,
drawing lines of fire wherever he touched. He might
as well have taken a felt pen to her chest, marking
her as his.

The slow circling of his thumbs was like a drug.
She stared at him, transfixed, her body turning to
liquid, her breasts aching, full and heavy. The heat
of his hands burned through her silk blouse. She felt
her nipples harden, press taut against the cups of her
bra and flimsy blouse. She felt so obvious, her desire
so transparent.

"I'm not shallow," she repeated, suddenly longing for more from him.

"You do love him, then!"

The rough intensity in Nic's voice surprised her.
Her head jerked up, and she stared into his narrowed
eyes. He waited for her answer, and her mind raced,
trying to decipher just where he was going with this
conversation.

And then it struck her. Nic, lovely, old-fashioned,

moral Nic, wanted to believe that Meg's mistake had been an act of passion, an act of *love*.

Love. If she loved Mark, Nic would understand. He might feel more benevolent regarding her mistake.

"Yes," she whispered, balling one hand behind her back.

"Then what can possibly be more important than giving your baby a father? A family? Maggie, what's keeping you two apart?"

"Nic—"

"Don't lie to me, Maggie. We've been through too much together for you to start lying now."

She stared helplessly into his face, needing more than ever to have him on her side, to have him be her friend. Her parents were distant. Mark was definitely not available. Folks in Healdsburg had always criticized everything she'd done. If only Niccolo cared.

If only she could trust him again.

"Talk to me, Maggie."

She drew a deep breath, praying for courage. "He's already married," she said quietly.

"What?"

His voice sounded like ice. Frighteningly smooth and yet hard, brittle, sharp. Shiver after shiver streaked down her spine. "Mark's been married for nearly ten years."

Nic's hands fell from her shoulders. He took a step backward. He looked at her with horror.

Please, don't look at me this way! Please understand, Nic.

"Tell me this is a joke." His voice rasped. "Tell me this is one of your bad attempts at humor."

A lump swelled in her throat, threatening to seal it. "I wish I could."

"Oh, Maggie!"

She flinched, her shoulders lifting to ward off the harsh censure in his voice. Didn't he understand how much she needed him? Didn't he realize how alone she felt?

Niccolo took another half step away, rubbed his jaw and turned to her, completely nonplussed. "You had an affair with a married man?"

"It wasn't exactly an affair—"

"Please, don't mince words. Mark, this man, he's been married nearly ten years?"

Slowly, she nodded, her body almost numb.

"Then he must have children?"

"Two," she said in a small voice.

"Maggie!"

"I didn't know he was married, Nic. I didn't know until it was too late."

Nic didn't answer her. Didn't look at her. He kept rubbing his jaw, his dark lashes hiding his expression. After what seemed like eternity he said, "Don't you even bother to find out anything about the men you sleep with?"

She jerked as if he'd struck her. "New York's not a small town. People don't know each other—"

"Then what were you doing sleeping with a stranger?" Nic snarled, his jaw thick, his hands clenched at his sides.

Meg felt a moment of fear. "I broke it off as soon as I learned the truth, but by then I was already pregnant."

"He won't leave his wife, will he?"

She dropped her gaze, humiliated. "No. Mark says he loves her—"

Nic's harsh laughter silenced her, the words dying on her lips. "Mark sounds like a truly upstanding man." He gritted the words out, digging his heel into the sand. "Just the kind of man you want to father your children, Maggie. You should be proud. Damn proud."

She shriveled inwardly, ashamed of herself despite her resolve. Nic had effectively reduced her to the size of a pea. No, less than a pea. A bug. A flea. Something incredibly small and lowly to be squashed beneath his heel.

Her lips parted in protest, some kind of defense on her tongue, but she didn't speak. There really was nothing to say. Nic was right, of course. Mark wasn't the kind of man she would have picked to father her children. She'd always believed that man would be strong, compassionate and ethical.

Ethical. Like her father. Her father, the last in a long line of California ranchers, was a man of his word. People liked him because he was honest and straightforward. He didn't play games. If he offered his help, he gave it.

Maybe that's one reason her dad and Niccolo got along so well. Niccolo might be considerably more wealthy, but they were cut from the same cloth.

Her mouth pursed at the irony.

Her father always did the right thing. Just like Nic. Unlike Mark.

Unlike herself.

She suddenly saw herself through Nic's eyes, and her stomach dropped. No wonder he treated her like a child. He saw her as impulsive and emotional, an immature woman who refused to take responsibility for her actions.

That wasn't who she was. He didn't know that she'd pushed herself to become financially independent as soon as she left home. She'd struggled to make her own way rather than turning to her parents for help. There were times when she lived in New York that she'd felt utterly alone, and yet instead of worrying her parents with her loneliness, she'd buried herself in her work, devoted extra time to making new friends. She hadn't set out to fall in love with a married man. He'd been someone she met at the Smithsonian Museum. He'd been attentive and attractive, and she'd found him interesting.

But that was neither here nor there. Her good intentions didn't matter, at least, they didn't matter to Nic and they wouldn't matter to her father. He'd be as livid as Niccolo, and even more disappointed.

The pain inside her was almost more than she could bear. She'd decided years ago to rely on no one, and yet relying on no one meant she had no one to turn to. She was twenty-eight, reasonably successful, financially solvent, but she was most definitely alone.

Now, for the first time in years, she couldn't bear to be alone. She needed her family, needed her friends. She needed to know that her baby would be part of a community that would love her and cherish her baby's growth.

It was agonizing to admit, but she needed help. She desperately needed support.

She needed Nic.

"Niccolo—"

Abruptly he held up a hand, silencing her. "Don't talk to me." His voice was harshly unforgiving.

With a wave of his hand, he dismissed her, then turned and strode to the car.

Something broke free inside her chest, and she nearly screamed.

He'd never walked away from her before. He'd never abandoned her in her life.

Relentless waves of pain swept through her. Wave after wave of fear and grief and loneliness. He didn't understand that she'd always needed him. He didn't understand that he was the one person in the world who made her feel safe and sane and special. He was the man she adored.

He didn't know, and if he did, he didn't care. He continued to walk away, the wind whipping his shirt, his long legs carrying him toward the stairs and the parking lot.

No, no, no. He couldn't walk away from her now. Couldn't turn his back on her. If he believed in her, she could do anything.

Meg slipped off her leather heels and ran after him, chasing him across the sandy dunes to the rickety wooden stairs. The moist salt air sparkled in her hair. Fine droplets clung to her skin.

Panting, she caught up with him by the stairs. Meg grabbed the back of his shirt, nearly tugging the olive green linen fabric from the waistband of his chino slacks. "Nic!"

He didn't shake her off but he didn't turn around.

"Nic, please—"

"What? What do you want me to say? Good luck, Maggie, have a great life, Maggie?" Fury and pain throbbed in his voice, his Italian accent growing more pronounced. "Is it my approval you want, *cara*, while you toss your life away? Should I say, 'Well done, darling,' and cut you a check for your baby's savings account?"

"Stop it!"

"Is it a baby shower you want? Or a crib for the side of your bed?" He came down a step, caught her wrists and dragged her level with him. "Are you in need of children's storybooks or Irish linen for the christening gown? Maggie!" He nearly roared her name, his golden eyes turning amber with pent emotion. "What do you want me to do? What do you want me to say?"

He'd been shaking her, a shake for each question. By the time he'd finished she was crying.

"Just be my friend!" she begged.

His hands fell away. "Your friend?" He drew a ragged breath, pushed his dark hair from his brow with an unsteady hand. The ocean waves thundered in the background, wave after wave crashing on the shore. Clouds gathered.

The air smelled so strongly of salt that Meg's nose burned.

"Your friend?" he repeated. His tone changed, and there was a peculiar expression in his eye. "Just like I was your friend all those years ago when I let you take the blame for Jared's mistake? When I stood by and did nothing? When I looked the other way despite the fact that you were in way over your head?"

She stared at him, transfixed. She'd never heard him speak with so much anger and passion, and yet he was utterly coherent.

"Is that the kind of friend you need, Maggie?"

He barked a laugh, the short, acerbic sound so raw and savage it made her chest ache. "Someone like Mark, right?"

The breeze caught her hair, blew the curls around her face in wild disorder. Nic stared at her, his brow furrowed. "No. No, Maggie, I can't be your friend." There was sympathy in his voice, sympathy and a note of pained tenderness.

She'd lost.

She'd lost him, lost everything. Unconsciously, she'd counted on him, believing he'd be there for her to help her, support her as she became a single mother. In the past Nic had been the first one to take her side. But no more. She'd lost his respect. She'd lost what little they had shared.

Meg couldn't speak, her pain so intense that it hurt just to breathe. She wanted to say his name, wanted to touch him, find him, somehow save them, but her throat closed and her heart twisted. She was too stricken to put thoughts into words.

Please, Nic. Please, Niccolo.

"Maggie, you told your mother that she would come home to a wedding. And she shall."

Niccolo drove swiftly, steering with one hand while rapidly punching numbers into his cell phone with the other.

"Carolyn, Niccolo Dominici here. Listen, I need your help. Can you pull something together for me? It's rather short notice, but I'm thinking of Saturday, just over a week from now. About a hundred guests, give or take a few. Sit-down dinner. Black tie. Elegant food, the best of everything."

He frowned, listening, and then with a caustic

glance at Meg, said, "Actually, yes, it is a special occasion. I'm getting married."

Meg pressed one knuckled fist against her mouth, listening in horror. Niccolo couldn't be serious.

"Yes, the reception will be at the villa. The ballroom, of course, and perhaps cocktails and appetizers in the garden."

"Hang up," she ordered. "This is ridiculous!"

He ignored her and described the wines he planned on serving, adding something about importing a dozen cases of the finest French champagne. Meg couldn't believe he was seriously considering arranging a wedding. Not just any wedding, *their* wedding.

"Nic!"

He raised a finger to his lips, shushing her.

Her fingers itched to snatch the phone from his ear and toss it out the window. "Nic, I'm serious."

He shrugged and continued with his conversation. Meg rolled her eyes, crossed her arms and glanced at the passing scenery. The car was eating up the miles, flying down the freeway, but they weren't heading to Napa.

Nic hung up and prepared to dial another number.

"Nic—"

"Not now, *cara*, I'm busy."

"You're wasting your time."

He punched in the rest of the number. "*Amore*, yes, it's Niccolo. How are you? Excellent. I have a favor to ask you. Would it be possible to stay open late? Yes, for me. Actually my fiancée. You hadn't heard? Well, it's happened quickly. She's an old family friend. I think you'll like her. We should reach the city around eight. See you then."

Nic hung up again.

"Where are we going now?" she demanded.

"Into the city. We'll buy your bridal gown and accessories tonight."

"An off-the-rack gown? How common." Meg couldn't help making the dig. She was exhausted, tired beyond belief, and Niccolo's little game was not sitting well with her.

He named a well-known designer, then shot her a dark look. "Not so common."

"Does he do wedding dresses?"

"He should have something formal and elegant." He cast her another dark glance. "And as we both well know, it doesn't have to be white."

Meg's stomach suddenly cramped. She bit her lip, resenting Nic, hating the nausea. She'd been feeling fine until he started his bully routine.

"You better stop the car," she warned, her stomach heaving, her head beginning to throb.

"You can't run from me."

"Fine. But pull over or I'll be sick in your pristine vintage Ferrari."

The drive into San Francisco was more like a snail's crawl in snarled, congested traffic through the foothills and across the striking Golden Gate Bridge. The traffic downtown was equally sluggish, and Niccolo's bad mood grew blacker. By the time they reached the boutique, he was white-faced and thin-lipped. His hard cheekbones pressed against his skin, and his strong jaw jutted in wordless fury.

Inside the store, Niccolo watched, silent and hawk-like, as she tried on dress after dress, only to reject each gown with a careless wave of his hand.

Nic finally picked a gown out of a design book,

the sheath sleekly sophisticated with a daring slit up the back. "In white," he said shortly, with a cool curl of his upper lip. "My Maggie looks lovely in white."

By the time Niccolo had settled on the dress, it was nearly midnight, and Meg drooped with fatigue.

Without consulting her, Niccolo drove them to a small, exclusive hotel at the top of Nob Hill where they were immediately ushered into an elevator and swept to the top floor.

Theirs was a penthouse suite, two bedrooms with private baths opening off an elegantly chic living room decorated in gold, pale yellow and cream. Meg took six steps into the living room before sinking in exhaustion onto one of the matching caramel-colored sofas covered in the softest buttery leather.

Her head fell back on the down-filled cushion. She closed her eyes and drew a deep breath.

She felt Nic approach, became aware of his presence before she heard him drop his keys on the marble coffee table.

"Can I get you something?" he asked, politely formal, as politely formal as he'd been all evening.

"No." She paused, opened her eyes, her gaze briefly meeting his before she looked away. "Thank you."

He said nothing, nor did he move. He stood in front of her, staring at her. She knew he was disgusted with her. She felt his long, slow scrutiny as his gaze traveled the length of her, resting first on her face, then her breasts, her hips, her legs. It was a look of ownership, of possession. He was assessing his goods, taking stock of this new fiancée of his.

"Satisfied?" she whispered, a knot of emotion forming in her chest.

"As satisfied as I can expect to be."

She would have smiled if she could. "You're a very hard man to please, Mr. Dominici."

He didn't answer, turning on his heel to open a tall mahogany sideboard lined with bottles and glittering glasses.

She watched him draw out two crystal snifters from the top shelf, along with a bottle of liqueur. He broke the seal on the bottle and poured a tiny mouthful into one snifter and a very liberal measure into the other.

He returned with the glasses, leaning over to hand her one.

She could smell the potent liqueur. Brandy. Oranges. Grand Marnier. "I can't drink," she said.

"One sip. A toast."

Her eyes burned, and she blinked. "Just what are we toasting, Nic?"

Her soft voice sounded as bruised as her heart felt. She and Nic had been through so much together, but what he suggested, what he was pushing them into, was incomprehensible. She might be attracted to him, might fantasize about making love with him, but that was a far cry from marrying him.

"To us," he answered sardonically, lifting his glass. The crystal snifter glittered in the soft, incandescent lighting. The amber-colored liquid swirled in the glass. He stared at her over the rim of his glass, his lower lip curled, his eyes hard. He looked cold and cruelly determined. It crossed her mind for the first time that perhaps she didn't know Nic as well as she'd thought. If he was capable of forcing her into marriage, he could be capable of any number of things.

Meg suppressed a shiver. "Us?"

"Of course, it's all about us now."

The careless laughter in his voice stung. He was taunting her, mocking her naïveté and innocence. The grittiness in her eyes grew worse. She blinked, trying to keep the tears from forming. "You'll destroy our friendship, Nic. You'll take what we are, what we've been, and change it forever."

The corner of his mouth lifted. "That has already happened. It took place years ago when I let you pretend you were driving the night of the accident. It changed when I stood by and let your father's heart harden against you. It changed when people in town gossiped about you and I turned a deaf ear to the slander. It did change, just as we changed. So you see, *cara*, we're not really risking all that much."

"But marriage?" She choked. "I know I'm not the wife you wanted."

His eyes narrowed, his hard jaw tightening grimly. He subjected her to another slow, objective perusal. "No," he coolly admitted, "and apparently I'm not the man you wanted."

CHAPTER SIX

"WAKE up. You have a doctor's appointment in an hour."

Meg rubbed her eyes, propped herself on her elbow and focused with great difficulty on Nic's silhouette in the doorway. "A doctor's appointment?"

"Downtown, in an hour."

She stared at him blankly. "I'm not sick."

"It's with one of San Francisco's leading obstetricians. I thought it made sense to have him check you over and get some blood work done."

"Blood work? Whatever for?"

He smiled thinly. "Maybe I want to see what I'm getting."

"What about an ultrasound? That'd give you more ammunition."

"Excellent suggestion, *cara*, I'll ask Dr. Collins to schedule one of those, too."

He wasn't joking. He was serious! Her insides felt like they were icing over. "You have no right to make appointments for me, Niccolo."

He dismissed her with a shrug. "Somebody needs to. You're not taking care of yourself."

"Nic, I'm thin, I'm not anorexic!"

He shrugged and leaned against the door frame. "That's neither here nor there. I think we should get a professional opinion and have a check done on your iron levels. You don't want to jeopardize the baby's health by being anemic."

He made her sound as if she were being irrational, and yet there was nothing irrational about not wanting him to dictate to her.

She had her own physician in Manhattan. She'd already had two prenatal appointments, including one very thorough workup. Her blood work had come back just fine, and even though she'd hadn't gained much weight, her doctor assured her that was fine for the first trimester. Some women gained a healthy amount right away, others put on weight during the second and third trimesters. It all depended on body type.

"I'm taking prenatal vitamins with *iron*," she answered tersely, sitting up and pressing the sheet to her bare chest. "If you'd like to see my medical chart, I can request that a copy be sent to you."

"That's not necessary. I'm sure Dr. Collins is happy to start his own file."

"Perhaps I should have Mark fax his pedigree papers?"

Nic's cold smile faded. "Get dressed. Now."

She shivered inwardly, shocked by his tone, but she would never let him see how much he unnerved her. "I'm not going."

"You are going." He turned, disappeared into the adjoining suite and reappeared with a small tray. Niccolo slid the tray in front of her. "Coffee, not too strong, enough for one cup."

"You're so amazing."

"Thank you."

Her mouth pursed as she bit back the retort that she didn't mean it as a compliment, but as an insult. He was amazingly egotistical. Amazingly domineering. Amazingly sure of himself.

Meg pushed the tray aside. Clutching the sheet tighter, she slid her legs over the edge of the bed, groping for a bathrobe. "Somehow I think you care less about my health than you do about the baby's possible birth defects."

Niccolo paled, looking almost ashen beneath his golden tan. "Nonsense."

"Is it? You're marrying me out of obligation. You're promising to raise my child as a Dominici. Of course you want a medical workup. You want to make sure your adopted daughter or son meets your snooty standards."

He froze, his immense shoulders stilling, his powerful body tensing.

She'd said too much. She knew it right away.

Scathingly, his gaze dropped to the rise of her breasts peeking from the sheet, and to the shadow of her cleavage. With another caustic perusal, he dismissed her, his expression cold and utterly disgusted. Niccolo turned and walked out, closing the door firmly.

With her heart in her throat, Meg slipped her arms into the hotel's white terry-cloth robe and tied the thick sash firmly about her waist. She waited for Nic to return, but he didn't. After several minutes she poured her coffee, the single cup Nic had mentioned, sat cross-legged on the bed and sipped the coffee in between worrying her lower lip.

She shouldn't have said such a thing to Nic. She owed him an apology, but the words stuck in her throat. He just made her so angry. He pushed all the right buttons every time.

Sighing, she encircled the cup with both hands,

clutching it for warmth as well as courage. She might not agree with this doctor's appointment, but she couldn't ignore Nic. Then there really would be hell to pay.

Meg swung open the door, tightened the sash on her robe and tiptoed into the living room.

He was at the desk near the bay window, on the phone. He briefly glanced at her before returning his attention to the call. After several minutes he hung up. He looked at her but said nothing.

"What if the baby did have a birth defect?" She jammed her hands into the robe pockets. "What would you do then?"

"Get help. Inquire with specialists." He leaned back in the chair and ran a hand through his dark hair. "Some defects can be mended in utero."

Some of the ice thawed around her heart. She felt like a heel. "What if the defect was quite serious? What if nothing could be done?"

He stared at her long and hard, his black brows lowered, his expression incredulous. "Maggie, this is your baby we're talking about. Not a thing. Not a monster. A baby. What do you think I'd do?"

His gaze held hers. She felt him pull her in, swallow her whole. "Mark didn't want the baby," she answered in a small voice. "He insisted on an abortion. He made an appointment with a clinic in New York and said I had to go, or he'd—" She couldn't finish. The words were too horrible to speak out loud.

"He'd what?" Niccolo demanded savagely.

"Drag me there himself."

"You're making this up!"

She shivered and turned away. "I wish I was."

"How could you love such a man?" His voice

dripped disdain and disgust. "How can you be so desperate to please a man that you'd—"

"But I didn't!" She whirled around. "Obviously, I didn't get an abortion. I left New York. I came—" She almost said *home*. Hastily she substituted. "Here."

Nic's lip curled. He looked at her as though she were the lowest form of life. No one but Nic made her feel so worthless. Meg blinked, hating herself for caring so much about his opinion.

"I know this baby is healthy," she said, lifting her chin, her eyes burning, hot and gritty, "but even if he or she wasn't, I'd never abort the baby. Never in a million years."

"So, we do have something in common."

Nic sighed and ran his fingers through his hair again, ruffling the dark black waves. It struck her for the first time that he looked weary, bone weary. "This marriage," he said slowly, thinking before speaking, "it's not going to be easy. It won't be impossible, it's just not…natural."

"No." She laughed shakily, hugging the terry-cloth robe tighter. "It's definitely not natural."

"But that doesn't mean we can't make it work. We just have to try harder."

"Niccolo, don't you think this has gone far enough? You've made your point."

"Made my point? *Cara*, this isn't football."

"Obviously, but I thought you'd back off from the marriage discussion by now. You're not really going to go through with this."

"Oh, yes, *we* are."

"Niccolo, marriage isn't like starting a business. We're talking about sharing lives, becoming intimate.'' Meg regretted the blush that swept her face, making her feel ridiculously immature, but she had to see this conversation through to the logical conclusion.

"And?"

Perhaps Nic didn't really mean a *marriage* marriage. Maybe he was thinking of something less personal. ''Maybe I'm misunderstanding you. Maybe you mean something in name only, an arrangement—''

"That would be convenient, wouldn't it?'' he interrupted curtly, his expression hardening, his mouth pressed into an immobile line. ''You have your baby, you have your safety net, you have freedom to take lovers on the side.'' He shrugged. ''Sorry, Maggie, I'm not that altruistic. Our marriage would be *real*.''

Shocked, she could only stare at him while a thousand disjointed thoughts raced through her head. A real marriage. Naked, beds, sex. Niccolo making love to her. Niccolo—

She jerked her head up, met his gaze. He smiled faintly, eyes gleaming, as if he knew exactly what she'd been thinking.

Before he could say another word, she returned to her room, shutting the door behind her.

Meg sat on the hotel bed, arms encircling her bent legs. She wished she could curl up and disappear. Her life was careening wildly out of control. It was one thing to become a mother. It was another to marry Nic and become *his* wife.

Niccolo's wife.

The very thought made her shiver. Nic wasn't the man she thought he was. He was harder, fiercer, more determined than she'd given him credit for. If he said their marriage would be real, he meant it.

Her heart thumped double time as she tried to imagine life with Niccolo. What kind of lover would he be? She knew he wasn't lacking in experience, but would he be tender or aggressive? Generous? Selfish?

Suddenly she pictured his hands, his mouth, and warmth flooded her limbs. No, he wouldn't be selfish. Far from selfish. If anything, he'd drive her wild.

Meg dropped her head, resting her cheek against the back of her hand.

But was that reason to marry Nic?

The door opened. Niccolo stood in the threshold. "Why aren't you dressed?"

She glanced at him, toes curling into the soft comforter tossed across the bed. "This will never work. We don't—"

"Love each other?" He completed the sentence for her.

Meg slid off the bed. "No, we don't, and a love-less marriage would be miserable."

"Not necessarily. We know each other, we understand each other, I'm sure we'd enjoy sex together."

Why did he have to keep talking about sex? It completely unnerved her, made her feel incredibly inexperienced. Niccolo would know all sorts of things, and she would... A blush scorched her cheeks as she pictured herself naked in his bed.

She'd be putty in his hands.

Rivulets of desire chased away her fear. Hunger coiled in her belly, and her nipples tightened expectantly. If only Nic would stop moving toward her. If only she'd stop skittering around the bed. He was like a tiger about to pounce, and she felt no bigger than a mouse.

Nervously, Meg touched the tip of her tongue to her upper lip, acutely aware that she was naked beneath the robe.

"Cat got your tongue, Maggie?" he softly taunted, closing in on her.

Her gaze darted right and left, seeking an escape, but the bed blocked her on one side and Niccolo stood on the other. For a moment she considered scrambling across the mattress but cringed at such a childish retreat. Trapped, she could only stand up to him. With far more bravado than she felt, Meg threw back her shoulders and braced her hands on her hips. "Excuse me, I'd like to dress. Would you kindly get out of my room?"

Nic leaned forward, placed an arm on either side of her shoulders and gazed into her upturned face. "If you want to dress, dress. I'm not stopping you."

She smelled his citrusy sandalwood cologne and a hint of spearmint on his breath. He'd shaved already, and his jaw appeared impossibly hard, his face bronzed angles and planes that made her fingers itch to touch him. Furious with herself for even thinking such a thought, she unleashed her anger at him. "It's a little hard to strip with you holding me captive."

His eyes lit up at the word *strip*. They grew brighter at *captive*. Meg silently cursed herself. "Mm, now there's an idea. Bondage. So you do like erotic games."

Heat surged through her, her face burning with chaotic emotions. "You're disgusting!"

"Liar, liar, pants on fire," he softly taunted, reaching out to stroke her feverish cheek. "You rather like the idea of me playing erotic games with you. After all, you started them ten years ago when you slid across my lap in nothing but a schoolgirl skirt and a very sexy, very lacy garter belt.''

''I was stupid.''

''You were curious.'' His finger drew an invisible line from her cheek down her neck, across her breastbone and up with tantalizing brevity across the tip of one nipple. ''And the truth is, you're still curious. I see it in your eyes every time I come near you. I feel it in your body every time I touch you. I hear it in your breath—''

''What nerve! What an ego! You're so incredibly full of yourself, Niccolo Dominici, you actually believe I'm still in love with you.''

''Not in love,'' he corrected, tilting her chin. ''But in lust.''

''No.''

''Yes. But it's not one-sided, Maggie. I'm just as enamored with you. You think I'm marrying you simply out of the goodness of my heart? Far from it. I want you. It's that simple. But I'll put a ring on your finger, make it legal, and then I'll enjoy you. Again and again and—'' his voice dropped a pitch ''—again.''

''I am not attracted to you, and I will not let you just use me like some common—''

''Be careful,'' he warned, hushing her with the tip of his finger. ''Be very careful, Maggie. Do not cast stones. You're in a precarious position, and I find your modesty act a bit overwrought.''

''How dare you!''

His eyebrows lifted. ''Maggie, you slid across my

lap at sixteen, your bare bottom on my lap and in my hands.''

She bristled, hands balling into fists, but before she could speak, he continued. ''You lay around the pool in swimsuits so skimpy they barely cover your…assets. You've slept with just about anyone, including married men—''

To hell with him! Let him burn in hell and rot his soul and—

She clenched her hands, longing to throw a quick jab. What she wouldn't give to bloody his perfectly straight, perfectly lovely Italian nose. ''For your information, I've been so busy with my career that I've dated very little!''

''No, you don't date. You indulge in affairs.''

''Not affairs. One relationship.'' She interrupted again, her temper blazing, blood roaring through her head, making her ears buzz. ''One relationship with one man. *One*, Nic. Not legions. Not dozens. Not two. One.''

''And he was married.''

''I made a mistake.''

''That's always your excuse, isn't it, Maggie?''

Bastard. He was quite a bastard. Scalding tears filled her eyes, but she gritted her teeth and blinked hard to keep them from falling.

Nic yawned and with a glance at his watch reminded her of the doctor's appointment. ''You've wasted a half hour. We've got twenty minutes left. I advise you to go shower and dress now. You need the time. You're not the wash-and-go type.''

Red-hot fury surged through Meg. ''Get lost!''

''What's wrong? Did I hit a sensitive nerve?''

So this was how it was going to be. Niccolo would

marry her, give her baby a name, but he'd humiliate her every chance he could, reducing her to something sordid and cheap. Her gaze met his and held. She'd never felt so much anger and hate for one person as she did just then for Nic. He wasn't just cold, he was harsh and cruel.

"I'll never marry you," she said, her voice strangled, her chest rising and falling with great gasps of air. "Being your wife would be pure torture. *Yes, Mr. Dominici. No, Mr. Dominici. How high, Mr. Dominici?* Forget it. I'd sooner put a hole in my head than put your ring on my finger!"

He clapped politely, a lazy smile curling his upper lip. "Well done, *cara*, you have a gift for the dramatic. Perhaps when the children are older and you've some time on your hands, you can audition for the community theater."

"Why are you treating me like this?"

His smile never wavered, his golden eyes gleaming. "Like how, *cara*?"

"Like I'm cheap. Like I'm beneath you."

"You're not beneath me, not yet. But on our wedding night, now that's another matter."

Her stomach cramped, and resentment burned within her. She would not stand here and take his insults. "There won't be a wedding night. I'm not going to marry you."

"Of course you will. It's been decided."

"It's been undecided. I will not marry you. Not now. Not ever. Don't you understand?"

"You've just wasted another minute. You don't want to see Dr. Collins in that bathrobe, do you?"

"Are you listening to me?"

"I heard what you said, but I don't think you've thought this all the way through."

"What's there to think through?"

His gaze met hers, hard and unyielding. "I see. So that's your final decision?"

She didn't answer, and after a moment, Niccolo turned and walked out of the bedroom.

She followed him to the door, watching as he reached into the living room closet and took his suit coat from the hanger. Nic swung the coat over his shoulders, sliding one arm into a sleeve, then the other. He eased the coat over his shoulders and smoothed his lapels flat. "I hope you've thought this through, *cara*. Considered the implications."

"Implications?"

"The implications of telling your parents the truth. Telling them what really happened the night Jared died." His grave expression changed, a light appearing in his golden eyes, a small smile curving his mouth, making him look quietly victorious. "What else did you think I meant?"

"This has nothing to do with Jared's death."

"Oh, but it does, my Maggie. You see, if I'd stepped forward and told the truth years ago, I think you'd have a different relationship with your father today. Indeed, I think you'd be a different person today."

"That's ludicrous!"

"Is it? You've spent more than a decade trying to forget the past. At least ten years carving a new identity for yourself. Obviously, the past causes you great pain." He checked his coat pocket for his wallet and reached into another for the valet parking ticket. "Anyway, that's a matter of opinion, and we're wasting time. What I'm offering you is marriage. I'm offering you and your baby emotional stability, financial security and respectability.''

Of course, respectability. Everything always came back to appearances with Nic.

Nic continued, unfazed by the anger in her eyes. ''But I'm not making threats and I won't hold you hostage. If you want to leave, you know where the door is. But if you leave now, know this. I shall never make my offer again, and I promise you, I will tell your parents the truth about Jared and the problems he'd been having with his drinking his last year at college.''

She froze, suddenly very, very tired. She hadn't thought he knew. They'd never once talked about the drinking before. ''You...knew?''

''I knew he'd been having problems for awhile, and I knew his university was close to suspending him. I interceded, offered to help Jared get counseling. They put him on academic probation instead.''

''Did you get him counseling?'' she asked, her voice faint to her ears.

''No.'' The bitterness in Nic's voice stung her. ''I drank with him on Christmas Eve and then let him climb behind the wheel. I might as well have killed him myself.''

Maggie turned a chair around and sat down rather heavily, her legs not quite strong enough to support her. ''No. That's not true,'' she whispered, reaching up to rub the back of her head, her soft curls loose, disheveled. ''Jared insisted on driving. He kept making a joke about someday competing in the Indy 500.''

Nic's mouth quirked, one corner lifting, and yet

there was only sorrow in his eyes. "Jared knew how to make us all laugh. He could be delightfully persuasive. But then, alcoholics generally are."

"Don't call him that."

"What? An alcoholic?" She winced, and Nic shook his head. "But Maggie, he was. Instead of getting him help we—I—looked the other way." He drew a ragged breath. "But I won't look the other way again. I'm here, Maggie, and I'm going to do the right thing by you. Now we don't have time to waste. I suggest you dress."

But still she hesitated. "You can't tell my parents about Jared. Not ever."

"I won't. As long as we stay married, the truth will remain here, buried, my secret. Our secret." And he tapped his chest, just above his heart. Pain filled his golden eyes, etched itself in lines around his beautiful mouth. "But it's up to you, Maggie. It's your choice."

She and Niccolo didn't speak in the doctor's waiting room. Nic pretended to read a magazine, and Maggie studied the framed prints on the wall, examining the still lifes as if they were great works of art.

Everything in the waiting room felt artificial, from the lavender and rose-colored upholstery on the sofas to the stiff arrangements of silk flowers on end tables. Long-stemmed pink flowers and purple hydrangea.

Fake.

Fake flowers. Fake ambience. Fake engagement.

"Mrs. Dominici?"

The waiting room door had opened. A nurse with a clipboard stood in the doorway.

Meg glanced around, as if a Mrs. Dominici would

appear. Nic stood up, gestured for Meg. "Come," he said.

Come. Sit. Stay.

"It's not Mrs. Dominici," she explained. "It's Margaret Buckner. *Miss* Margaret Buckner."

The nurse glanced at the chart, confused. "Ah, I'm sorry, we have you down as Maggie Dominici."

Nic's fingers wrapped around her arm just above her elbow. "She'll be Mrs. Dominici very soon," he replied smoothly, propelling Meg forward.

"How wonderful," the nurse remarked. "Where's the wedding going to be?"

"Napa."

Meg's stomach cramped. He made it sound so easy. A wedding in Napa. One hundred guests. Cases of champagne.

The nurse smiled at Niccolo with wide-eyed fascination. Meg shouldn't have been surprised. Nic affected every woman like that.

"Oh, I just *love* Napa," the nurse said, gushing. "All those darling bed-and-breakfasts, and the wineries are to die for. Do you have a favorite winery?"

"Dominici." Nic's expression gave nothing away.

"Like your name!" The nurse suddenly colored. "Oh, are you related to the Dominici wine makers?"

Nic inclined his head, and Meg ground her teeth.

With another bright smile in Nic's direction, the nurse gestured down the hallway. "We'll be going this way. But first Mrs. Dom—I mean, Miss, uh, Buckner—we'll need to weigh you and get a urine sample. Mr. Dominici, will you be coming with us?"

"Yes," he answered.

"No." Meg spun to face him. She placed two fingertips on his chest and pressed him back. "This is where I draw the line, Nic. This is my body and my appointment. Any information you want to know, you can find out after the examination is over.''

He smiled at the nurse and completely ignored Meg. ''Of course I'm coming. I want to know *everything* about our baby.''

CHAPTER SEVEN

NICCOLO dropped Meg off at the Hunts. She spent the rest of the afternoon sitting in a shady corner of the garden sketching plans. Except for serving her a glass of lemonade and discreetly inquiring about the family emergency, the Hunts left her alone, eager for her to continue work on the proposed renovation.

Meg was grateful for the chance to make progress on her drawings and attempted to focus on her sketches, but the events of the last twenty-four hours weighed heavily on her mind.

Not everything was bad. Like today's ultrasound. It had been absolutely wonderful. Miraculous, really. To see the baby inside her, to watch the little heart pump, see the tiny legs kick. The baby had been active, wiggling this way and that, and Meg's heart had leaped to her throat, silent tears filling her eyes.

Her baby.

The ultrasound revealed what she already knew. The baby was healthy and strong. Meg might not be gaining weight quickly, but her baby appeared well-nourished, moving constantly during the ultrasound.

Niccolo had been there, of course. He'd been silent at first as the doctor pointed out the four chambers of the baby's heart, highlighting the vertebrae of the spine and the formation of the arms and legs. But when the baby appeared to pop its thumb into its mouth, Nic took two swift steps forward and touched the monitor in awe.

Just remembering made Meg's eyes fill with tears. She couldn't remember when she had last felt so emotional. Everything was affecting her strongly. The baby. Memories of Jared. Niccolo.

Especially Niccolo.

Picking up her pencil, she tried to force herself to concentrate on her project, shutting out everything but the peaceful garden and the dancing shadows cast by the tall poplar trees.

But as the afternoon drew to an end, dusk creeping into the garden, muting the garden's brilliance, Meg felt a rush of worry and dread.

It was one thing to become a mother. But another to marry Niccolo. Unless he cared a little. That would change everything. Their marriage wouldn't seem so overwhelming if there was more to it than duty.

Duty.

The word stuck in her throat, echoed gratingly inside her head. It was the kind of word that made Meg want to run. Indeed, all her life she'd shaken off that which was expected of her and done the exact opposite.

Duty.

It was the worst reason for a man to marry her. The absolute worst reason to spend her life with Niccolo.

But even as she struggled with the pretense of the marriage, a carnal hunger for Nic, to be possessed by Nic, ricocheted through her, flaming her senses. She was shameless, truly, to want Niccolo this way. She knew what he thought of her, and yet somehow, in his arms, his mouth against hers, she felt more alive than she did at any other time.

* * *

Francesca was lighting the candles on the table when Meg arrived at the villa. "Dinner will be served at seven," she informed Meg.

Meg nodded, hesitating in the hallway to watch the housekeeper finish lighting the candles. She noted the three place settings on the imposing dining room table. Francesca never had dinner with Niccolo in the dining room, so there must be a guest joining them tonight.

"Who's coming for dinner?" she asked.

"Father Rivera. Niccolo's priest." Francesca leaned forward to adjust the wineglasses, lining them up precisely. She then straightened one of the gilded chairs. "Change quickly, Maggie. Father should be here any time."

Meg hadn't expected any great display of affection from Niccolo in front of the family priest, but neither had she expected him to be so chillingly aloof. Nic ignored her during dinner, failing to include her in his conversation—which he conducted mainly in Spanish for the Andalusian priest's benefit—nor did he make eye contact.

It was as if she didn't exist.

Meg was surprised by the depth of her hurt. Somehow, after the ultrasound appointment, after the day they'd spent together, she thought Niccolo was serious about making a go of the marriage, making it work, making them a family. But if this cold silence was his idea of family, well, he could take his marriage proposal and put it in a not-so-nice place.

Niccolo suggested an after-dinner walk, and the three of them strolled the estate's extensive grounds, pausing frequently so Father Rivera could sniff the late roses, all the while sharing with them his thoughts on marriage and the sanctity of the vows.

Meg's insides churned as Father Rivera talked, and she felt Nic's tension grow. Glancing at him from beneath her lashes, she noted his darkening expression, his brow lowered, his eyes narrowed and brooding. And still he didn't acknowledge her.

He didn't have to tell her he didn't like marrying her; it was written all over his face, emanating from every pore in his body.

Her hurt gave way to anger. It was ridiculous for him to sulk. This marriage hadn't been her idea. If he didn't like it, call it off.

They finished the slow circle through the garden and returned to the front steps of the villa. It was late, the moon shining dimly above, and after blessing them both, Father Rivera said good-night, then slowly made his way to his car.

Meg had somehow managed to keep a smile pasted on her face through the garden tour, but she'd had about enough of Niccolo's frigid demeanor. "We make a delightful couple, don't you think?"

Niccolo glanced at her and frowned. "We're fine."

"You don't think we lack any…warmth?"

"Father's a priest. He'd prefer us to behave discreetly. Or would you rather have him know the truth? That I'm marrying you only to give your baby a proper name?" Niccolo smiled, baring his teeth. She thought he looked distinctly wolflike. "I think not, Maggie. He's a dear friend of the family's, and there's really no reason to shock him."

She couldn't have said a word at that moment even

if she wanted to. She felt the blood drain from her face. "We were once friends."

"We still are, *cara*. Otherwise I wouldn't be jumping through hoops."

"I didn't ask you to jump through hoops."

"No, you didn't ask, because you don't think." Savagely, he turned and walked away.

Meg followed him into the winery cellar. Cool and dark, the cellar smelled pungent, ripe with fermenting grapes, the stone walls lined with dozens of massive oak barrels.

She spotted Nic climbing one of the barrels, and she circled it. It was nearly ten feet tall and dwarfed her. "We need to talk."

"We'll have plenty of time to talk after we're married," he answered, twisting a cap off and drawing a sample.

The wedding! It was just days away. "Nic, I know how seriously you take these vows. I also know this isn't what you want for yourself."

He sniffed the sample, then let a drop fall onto his tongue. Wincing, he said, "I'm willing to compromise."

The word *compromise* sounded sour in his mouth, much like the wine on his tongue. She didn't like the comparison, but it fit. "You've never compromised about anything. Why do it now?"

Nic screwed the barrel cap on and crouched, his muscular legs pulling his denim jeans taut across the thighs. His long black hair brushed his collar , a lock falling across his temple. "Looking to weasel out?" he softly asked.

Weasel out? "A lovely phrase, if I ever heard one."

He shrugged. "You're the one running scared."

"I'm not running anywhere. I'm asking if you're having second thoughts."

Nic stood up, jumped off the barrel. "Listen, *cara*, you're wasting your time, and you're wasting mine. This wedding is going to happen. Now if you'll excuse me, I have work to do."

He brushed past her, grabbed his cellular phone from his back pocket and quickly dialed a number.

"Nic, this conversation isn't over," she called after him.

Still walking, he turned, glancing at her over his shoulder. One of his black eyebrows raised, as if to mock her.

"Hello, Papa? Yes, Nico here," he said, switching to Italian and turning, effectively dismissing her.

Obviously, the conversation *was* over.

Niccolo managed to fill every minute during the next few days with business meetings, winery tours and public-relations planning sessions. He didn't have a minute to spare for her.

"Deal with them." That was all Nic said about the steady stream of visitors in and out of the villa anxious to discuss the coming wedding. The caterer, the florist, the musicians, the party rental company. The various businesses kept showing up, then returning with another list of details, questions and specifications.

The party rental company needed exact measurements to create a custom white canvas tent. The florist, on discovering that Meg was a landscape designer, wanted to know her favorite flower. The caterer wanted to be sure that Meg liked seafood, because three of the appetizers featured shrimp, scallops or crab.

And all Meg wanted was to escape to the Hunts and try to forget that this elaborate wedding would soon take place.

In the week before the wedding, as Meg labored over massive blueprints, Niccolo's shadow fell, darkening the plans and making it impossible for her to work.

"Why don't you have a cell phone?" he demanded irritably, dragging a hand through his black hair. "I couldn't reach the Hunts, couldn't contact you, and so I had to drop everything to drive over here."

"I'm sorry."

"Everybody has a cell phone."

"Not me." She pushed her sunglasses up, resting them on the top of her head. "What can I do for you, Nic? I'm assuming you have something on your mind?"

"Be home by six. We have an appointment with my lawyer."

Her heart did a strange flutter. His lawyer. That didn't sound good. "Do I need my lawyer present?" she asked sweetly, reaching for her sunglasses and placing them back on her nose.

"No. Not unless you're planning on presenting me with a prenuptial of your own."

A prenuptial agreement. Of course. Niccolo wouldn't leave any stone unturned. She drew her lips back, praying it looked like a smile. "I'll be there."

"Don't keep me waiting."

"Can't do that, can I? I'd hate to see you lose your sunny disposition."

*   *   *

Meg returned to the villa early enough to shower and change before dinner. Tonight of all nights she wanted to feel confident, and looking polished would certainly help make her feel more pulled together.

Ignoring the trepidation weighting her limbs, Meg slipped into black satin underwear, rubbed a scented lotion over her arms and legs, then fastened a black bra behind her back.

She wouldn't let Nic intimidate her. She wouldn't let him dictate to her, either.

Meg stepped into black silk trousers and pulled a long blue silk tunic over her head. The broad bands of gold embroidery at the neck, cuffs and hem made her feel elegant, if not just a little bit exotic. Rather Egyptian, she thought, twisting her hair up and pinning the curls into a sleek, sophisticated chignon.

Blue lapis and gold earrings, a gold bangle on her wrist. Meg stood back and checked her reflection, grateful that the royal blue tunic hid her pregnancy. She wanted to look poised, not maternal, not when she might possibly be called into battle.

A knock sounded on her door. ''Niccolo is waiting for you,'' Francesca announced through the door. ''He's in the library.''

The library? The last time Meg met Niccolo in the library she'd dabbed perfume behind her ears, fastened the beautiful new lace garter belt around her waist and stepped out of her cotton underwear.

Her full lips twisted wryly. A repeat scenario would not take place tonight.

Meg pushed open the library's massive oak door and stepped into the dark-paneled room. Her gaze swept over the fire glowing in the hearth, the brass lamp on Niccolo's reading table, the walls covered in leather-bound books. Everything looked the same, even the leather couch by the fire.

"You look lovely," Nic said, rising from his desk.

His friendly tone disarmed her, and the unexpected compliment flattered her, sending heat creeping into her cheeks. "Thank you."

The sleeves of his white linen shirt were rolled back, revealing strong bronzed forearms. He looked deceptively relaxed. Meg knew better. Niccolo did nothing by chance.

"Where's your attorney?" she asked, praying her voice sounded steady.

"He's been delayed at the office. We should expect him in an hour."

An hour? So long?

Nic moved from behind his desk to lean against it, the leather belt in his dark trousers accenting his narrow waist and the powerful length of his muscular legs.

He studied her slim figure, his gaze slowly wandering from the top of her head to the heels of her shoes. "If I hadn't seen the ultrasound last week, I wouldn't believe you're pregnant. It'll be interesting to see if you carry your second child so well."

Meg's throat sealed closed. "Second?"

"Ours, of course."

Ours. She swallowed with difficulty, her nerves jangled, her mouth dry. With a shaky step, she moved toward the hearth, putting another foot between them.

She couldn't help thinking he'd planned this. The lawyer had never been scheduled to show at six. Niccolo wanted to knock her off balance. It had been one of his business tactics—befriend the competition then move in for the kill.

"I'll want several," he added, a taunting light in his golden eyes. "Most Italian men do."

"And Italian women agree?"

"Oh, yes, most definitely. They enjoy the attention of their husbands. You see, *cara*, Italian men are supremely proficient lovers."

"Oh, please!"

"Please, what?" he answered, his deep voice dropping lower, his inflection suddenly husky. "Please show you?"

Meg moved another step back, crossing her arms over her chest, discomfited by the warmth in his voice and the gleam of possession in his eyes. He'd prepared her for a legal transaction, then turned personal.

She caught Nic's smoldering gaze and blushed.

Very, very personal, indeed.

Meg walked the perimeter of the room, careful to maintain a discreet distance from Nic.

"You like my books?" he drawled, intently watching her.

She feigned an interest in the floor-to-ceiling shelves. Truly, she'd never known anyone to own such an extensive library of antique books, particularly books devoted to the history of commerce and the role of Italy in early medieval trade. But of course Nic's library wouldn't just be a room lined with books. It was his retreat.

"Is there a book you're looking for in particular?"

His mocking voice drew her attention, yet the dangerous gleam in his eyes made her heart thump harder. Her nerves scraping like fingernails on a chalkboard, she felt terribly on edge.

She had to calm down. Needed to focus her energy, try to control her emotions. Blindly she stared at the framed map above the fireplace, which highlighted Spanish and Italian trade routes in the sixteenth century.

"It's an intriguing map," he said from behind her.

Rivulets of tension zigzagged through her. She felt her shoulders tighten. Her spine was exquisitely sensitive. "I've always been fascinated by this room," she answered with forced brightness, knowing she couldn't stare at the map forever.

Reluctantly, but aware that she had no choice, Meg turned to face him. "It's a beautiful room."

"You used to find my love of antiques peculiar."

"I didn't grow up with antiques. In our house, really old meant nineteen-fifties collectibles." She smiled faintly, amused by her former lack of sophistication. "Yet this is magnificent."

"I'm pleased you've…matured."

She pretended not to see the quirk of his mouth. He so enjoyed baiting her. It had become his favorite pastime.

Nic leaned against the desk, arms folded over his broad chest, pulling the white collar open and giving her a glimpse of the bronzed plane of his chest. "How long has it been since you were last here?"

"More than ten years," she said in a rush, not needing to count them.

"That's right. Isn't this the place you attempted to seduce me?"

"Actually, we were on the couch," she answered with bravado, smiling a dazzling smile, refusing to let him know how humiliating she found the memory.

"I stand corrected." He left the desk, moved to the leather couch and sat down. "This is where we were," he added, sliding his palm across the dark brown leather as slowly and lovingly as if the couch were wired with nerve endings.

Meg stared at his caressing hand, mesmerized by the tanned length of his fingers, the width of his palm. For a split second she longed to feel his hand on her, his palm cupping her breast, fingers grazing her nipple.

A frisson of warmth sparked within her. She felt him, was aware of him, in every nerve in her body.

Niccolo's eyes met hers and held.

It was as if he knew she was attracted to him, as if he could read exactly how she felt. Just like one of the books on his shelf...

Meg broke from his gaze, turned to face the fire and lifted her hands to the flames. They trembled as she held them up.

"Come here," he quietly commanded.

She resisted the quiet entreaty in his voice, hating the shiver that slid up and down her spine. "No."

Going to Nic would be like throwing herself in the flames. He'd burn her. Destroy her. She couldn't control her feelings around him, which made him the most dangerous man she knew.

"Maggie, I want you to come to me."

There was less entreaty in his voice, more force. He wanted her to obey him. He wanted to prove a point, to demonstrate that she still found him impossible to resist.

Her shoulders lifted, hair rising on her nape. She

found it very hard to say no to him. But then he knew that.

"Ah," he said after a moment, "you're afraid."

"I'm not."

"You are. Otherwise you'd come sit with me."

"Maybe I don't want to sit."

"Maybe you're afraid I'll make love to you."

Her lashes closed, her body drooping even as the most carnal craving shot through her. He tangled her up, catching her in a convoluted web of dread and need. He was right, of course. She was afraid he'd make love to her. She was afraid of the strength of her feelings.

If he touched her, she'd want more, so much more than a simple kiss, a brief caress. He'd unleash her most primitive passions.

Wishing to protect herself, she grasped at the first thing that came to mind. "But you don't want me," she answered sharply. "You've never wanted me. You told me quite clearly that you don't fancy me."

"Things change." He circled his hand on the leather cushion again, rubbing the surface with the tips of his fingers. "Remember, *cara*, we've changed."

"You haven't!" she answered with a trace of bitterness.

"Oh, yes, I have."

His voice vibrated within her. Her belly clenched, her inner thighs tensing. He was seducing her already, seducing her with words, teasing her mind, making her want him without even a touch.

"And you've changed, too. Once you weren't afraid of anything, and yet look at you now. Cowering in front of my fireplace."

"I'm not cowering!"

"Quaking, then." He laughed softly at her indignant expression. "I think you're afraid because you're no longer in charge. You've lost control."

"Your conceit is amazing!" Her voice sounded panicked even to her own ears.

"You will come to me." His eyes dared her to argue. When she didn't speak, he lifted a hand, extended it to her. "I know you, *cara*, and I'm waiting."

"You'll be waiting all night."

"Fine."

His eyes held her captive. She couldn't move. Couldn't speak. He stared at her, taunting her, making her painfully aware of the change in both of them.

He was right. They weren't the same people.

Her heart seemed to slow, stop, change tempo. Then suddenly, helplessly, she found herself moving toward him. She stopped abruptly in front of him, as if she couldn't possibly take another step. Her pulse raced, but her bones felt as if they were dissolving, turning her into warm, sweet honey.

Niccolo captured her wrist in his hand and drew her down on the couch. "No, that's not quite right," he murmured. "You were on my lap, isn't that so?"

With a precision that would have impressed a surgeon, Niccolo lifted her onto his lap, parted her knees, then pulled her snugly forward, high on his thighs.

White heat exploded deep inside her. With almost clinical detachment, Niccolo parted her knees wider, heightening her awareness, and Meg writhed inwardly, shamelessly carnal.

She'd let him do anything to her. She'd beg him to do everything.

"Nic, no, this—" She broke off as his palms slid up the insides of her thighs, the heat of his hands burning through the flimsy silk of her trousers.

"What was that?" he murmured, his golden eyes darkening with desire.

She had to go. She had to leave this very second or she'd never escape with her pride intact. Yet she couldn't bring herself to speak, too fascinated by the play of his hands along her hips, lifting her, cradling her, until he held her bottom.

He lifted her, adjusting her, placing her immediately above the rise in his tailored trousers. She gasped at the press of his erection and the sharp bite of his zipper against her most tender flesh.

His eyes bored into hers, and with a deliberate move, he took her knees in his palms and opened her wider still.

Meg gasped, felt her head go light. Rivulets of sensation screamed through her, her thighs tensing, her body quivering.

"Is this how it was, Maggie?" he murmured, still watching her intently, analyzing her response to each of his actions. "You were on my lap, like this, yes?"

CHAPTER EIGHT

WITH a rock of his hips, he pressed against her thin silk trousers, his erection penetrating part of the delicate fabric. She felt the tip of him against her, felt the heat and urgency of his desire. She was afraid to breathe, afraid to move, precariously positioned against the thrust of his rigid shaft.

"Now what?" he asked, his eyes narrowing, his black lashes lowering.

She could only shake her head, her brain dazed by the exquisitely intense sensations. Years ago she'd climbed on his lap, anxious to seduce him, longing to prove she was a woman. She'd failed, and Niccolo had never forgotten her childish lovemaking. Now he was showing her just what she'd missed.

She bucked slightly as one of his thumbs traced the seam of her silk trousers, running along the line of her most private place.

"Stop," she ordered, grabbing Niccolo's elegant white shirt, her thighs tightening, her body responding despite her attempt to shift off him.

"Why? This is what you wanted that night, isn't it?" He cupped her through her thin trousers, heightening her warmth, the palm of his hand pressed to her mound. Ripples of sensation rocked her, wave after wave of need. His palm moved up, down, teasing the tiny, tightened bud engorging with blood.

It was what she wanted. It was exactly what she

wanted, but she'd never admit it, not when he played with her, toyed with her, mocking her need.

Her tongue felt heavy, thick. She forced herself to speak. "I regret that night with all my heart," she said bitterly, almost overwhelmed by the effort to defend herself.

"So do I," he retorted with a harsh laugh. "I should have taken you then, given you what you wanted."

"Go to hell!"

Nic laughed before reaching up to clasp her face in his hands and draw her mouth to his. "If I go, you'll go with me," he muttered against her lips before his mouth crushed hers.

She welcomed the harshness of his mouth, welcomed the punishing pressure of his lips. At least this was strong, fierce, consuming. For days she'd felt strung out, tensely nervous. But this…this anger and passion she at least understood.

Meg answered his kiss with equal ardor. No longer was she a girl. She was now a woman. At least her relationship with Mark had taught her one thing, that she didn't want just sex, she wanted this, this torrid, volatile hunger she felt for Nic.

The kiss deepened, intensified, his lips parting hers with a hunger he couldn't hide. Meg only knew that she wanted more, needed more, and she clasped his face in her hands, lost in him, overwhelmed by his warmth and the smoothness of his strong jaw in her hands.

His tongue played against her lips, flicked her teeth before drawing her tongue into a slow, seductive dance. She leaned against him, her breasts pressed to the hard contours of his chest, her hips grinding against his lap. She felt him everywhere at once, yet nothing gratified, nothing answered her tremendous hunger.

Suddenly Niccolo lifted his head. He appeared as shaken as she felt. He gazed into her face, his golden eyes darkened to amber. "I should have taken you up on your offer a long time ago."

His laughter shocked her. Before she could move, he lifted her off his lap and dropped her onto the couch next to him. "That was delightful," he drawled, recovering his composure far more quickly than she. "I thought you'd be passionate, but you're…beyond passionate. You're wild."

His words, the taunt in his voice, were like a stinging slap on her already bruised ego. Meg scrambled off the couch, disgusted with herself and hating him with every fiber of her being. Nic wasn't just cruel. He was pure medieval malice. Hard to believe that men like him still existed in the twenty-first century.

She pointed a finger at him, jabbing it in midair. "Do not touch me again. Do not come within six feet of me. And if you do…"

"What, Maggie?" There was no anger in his voice, just lazy amusement and pointed curiosity about what she'd say. "What will you do?"

"I don't know. But I promise you, you won't enjoy it."

He stood, crossed to where she stood and gazed at her. "Oh, I wouldn't be so sure, my love. I have news for you. When it comes to the physical, when it comes to the senses, I'm just as base, just as desperate and just as carnal as you."

Base, desperate, carnal.

She felt his words and the mockery in his voice

all the way through her. Truly, he held her in low esteem. In his eyes she was loose, promiscuous. He'd never respect or love a woman like her.

She couldn't bring herself to speak. Her chest was tight with wretched emotion. She shouldn't have come home. Shouldn't have dreamed she could return.

Nic kissed the side of her neck, then trailed one fingertip from her earlobe to her exposed collarbone. She shivered at the fleeting caress.

He kissed her again, gauging her reaction. "I want you to realize that our marriage won't be without its rewards," he said huskily. "You might not love me, *cara*, but you will love what I will do to your body."

"Niccolo!"

"Margaret."

It was the first time in her life he'd ever called her by her given name. Meg swallowed painfully, her mouth so dry it felt as if she'd swallowed a fistful of cotton.

"Yes," he added, passion still smoldering in his golden eyes. "You will love what I do to you. You might glare at me. You might say you hate me. You might try to defy me. But thank God you're not indifferent to me."

With that he straightened, and adjusted his fine white linen shirt, looking crisp and coolly elegant. One wouldn't have known that anything intimate had transpired between them. "My lawyer has arrived. It's time you met him and we took care of this important bit of business."

The lawyer was far younger, and more attractive, than Meg expected. She'd pictured a middle-aged attorney with a thick Italian accent. Instead the tall, blond, athletic-looking Carl August turned out to be one of Niccolo's university friends. Niccolo mentioned that Carl specialized in corporate law, mainly mergers and acquisitions.

It was on the tip of her tongue to say that their relationship was not a merger and she definitely wasn't an acquisition, but thought better of it at the last second.

Over dinner Niccolo told stories of his boyhood in Tuscany. How he and his brother romped through the olive groves, played chase in the vineyards and generally made nuisances of themselves for staff and family at their four-hundred-year-old ancestral home. Meg ground her teeth. Niccolo waxed poetic, his descriptions as vivid as though he were reading a travelogue.

After dinner Francesca poured coffee in the living room before leaving them alone, discreetly closing the tall arched doors behind her.

Niccolo immediately dropped his genial manner. Setting his espresso cup down, he turned to Carl, asking for the documents he requested be drawn up that morning.

"The terms of the marriage agreement have been spelled out," Nic said without a trace of emotion. "As my wife, you will share equally in my wealth, family estates and stake in the Dominici wineries. If anything should happen to me, you, and our children, will inherit everything."

"Our children?" she murmured, balancing the china cup on her lap. "What about..." She glanced in Carl's direction, wishing he wasn't party to this private discussion. "What about my baby?"

"Your baby?" Nic's eyebrows flattened. "There is only our baby. Our babies. We're to be a family, Maggie. There is no yours, mine, his, hers. I thought I'd already made that clear."

Carl slid another set of documents across the glass-topped end table. Meg picked the documents up and skimmed the first page. Her troubled gaze met Nic's before returning to the document. "But how can you adopt the baby? Mark—"

"He's already signed the papers."

Her head jerked up, and she stared speechlessly at Niccolo.

Nic nodded, his dark head gleaming in the soft light thrown by the wall sconces. "Carl flew to New York this morning. He traced Mark, took him my terms, and Mark accepted."

"Your terms?" Shock gave way to anger. "Just what were your terms?"

"Don't look so appalled. They were quite reasonable."

"Tell me you did not buy this baby!" The stapled set of papers fell from her fingertips to the table. "Tell me you did not offer Mark money!"

Nic's gold eyes glittered hard. He didn't answer.

She clenched her hands into fists. "You did not, Nic, you *could* not!"

His lips curled, reminding her of a leopard about to pounce. "Don't look so shocked, Maggie. You knew I was ruthless. You've known for years that I get what I want." He held up a hand as her lips parted, silencing her. "But before you defend your beloved, let me tell you he took it, Maggie. And he didn't just take what was offered, he demanded more. Significantly more."

"No!"

"Yes. Your noble, moral Mark was more than happy to give his son up—" he broke off, contemptuously shaking his head "—that's right, *son*, to the highest bidder."

"Don't!" She screamed the word, clapping her hands to her ears and staggering to her feet. "Don't ever say you bought this baby. This baby was never for sale, and I don't want to know what he took, or what you paid."

She drew a deep, tremulous breath and dropped her hands to her chest, pressing them to her heart as if she could control the ragged thudding. She couldn't believe this was happening, couldn't believe Niccolo would do this to her, to the baby. "How could you, Nic?" she challenged.

A nerve popped in his jaw, and his eyes narrowed to slits. "I did it to protect you. And our son."

Son. He'd said it a second time. Through the film of tears clouding her eyes, she looked at him. "How do you know it's a boy?"

"The ultrasound. I could tell. It was…he was—" Nic's eyebrow arched "—unmistakably a boy."

She hadn't seen and she hadn't asked. She'd been too preoccupied with proving to Nic that the baby was healthy, that she was healthy, to ask about the baby's gender. Perhaps unconsciously she hadn't wanted to know, leaving it as a surprise.

A son. Maybe someone wonderfully funny and kind like Jared. Or someone cruelly self-serving like Nic.

"Let me see the papers," she demanded tersely, imperiously extending her hand.

Wordlessly Carl handed them to her. She felt Nic's

gaze as she examined the set of documents in which
Mark gave his consent for Niccolo to legally adopt
the baby. There was no mention of financial remu-
neration, no wrangling over terms. Just dry legal ver-
biage.

Ignoring Niccolo completely, she looked at Carl.
"Is it true? Did Mark accept money from Nic?"

The attorney glanced at Niccolo before nodding
briefly, his expression blank. "I don't think it's ac-
curate to say he took money for the baby, but yes,
there was a financial transaction."

A financial transaction. Incredible.

Meg turned to Niccolo. She stared at him with
undisguised dislike. She had obviously never known
him or grasped how ruthless he could be.

"You might think you've bought the baby from
Mark, but you haven't bought me. I am not, and will
never be, for sale."

Meg heard the front door close. With a glance out
her bedroom window she saw the attorney disappear
into his car. At last, he was gone.

Now she'd have her say.

Meg opened her bedroom door and marched down
the sweeping staircase. Niccolo was in the living
room, standing before the elaborate marble mantel,
staring into the fire.

Livid, she prepared to launch into a furious attack
on his underhanded tactics. But before she could
speak, Niccolo struck first.

"Well, well, that was quite a show."

Her mouth opened, shut. She was silenced by his
sarcasm. *Wait a minute,* her brain protested, *I'm the*

*one that's angry. I'm the one that has a bone to pick
with you.*

But again, without giving her a chance to speak,
he rebuked her.

"How can I help protect you and the baby if you
insist on behaving irrationally? Stomping in and out
like an irate five-year-old only makes you look foolish."

"Now, wait a minute, Niccolo Dominici. Sending
an attorney to meet with the competition might be
fair business tactics, but it's not acceptable when
dealing on a personal level. You had no right to contact Mark. You had no right to pursue the adoption
without discussing it with me first."

"What do you think I was doing tonight?" He
smacked his forehead in disbelief as he turned to face
her. "I was trying to have a discussion with you."

She laughed hollowly. "Semantics aside, a prenuptial agreement is not a discussion. Adoption paperwork is not a discussion. Intimidating me with
your attorney is *not* a discussion."

The corners of his mouth twitched. "Carl is not
an intimidating lawyer."

"Maybe not to you, because he's your old college
buddy and your personal attorney. Niccolo, don't you
understand what it felt like for me? I was alone in
there. I was alone and you had my back up against
the wall."

He was silent a moment, thinking. "You're right."
He looked truly apologetic. "I'm sorry. I should have
talked with you first."

"Thank you." She sank onto a soft suede-covered
ottoman and covered her face. Her body curled. Her
shoulders shook.

Suddenly Nic crossed to her side. "*Cara*, please don't cry." He ran his hand across the back of her head, smoothing her hair beneath his fingertips. His touch was gentle, comforting, more comforting than it had been in days.

"I'm not crying," she said, her voice a croak. She lifted her face to him. "I'm laughing. I'm laughing at how utterly ridiculous this all is. The very idea of us marrying is absurd. Niccolo, we don't see eye-to-eye on anything. How can we make a marriage work?"

His golden eyes stared into hers, his gaze so intense she couldn't look away. "You want what's best for the baby, yes?"

"Yes."

"You want to be sure that Mark doesn't ever hurt the baby the way he's hurt you, yes?"

"Yes."

He caressed her cheek with the back of his hand. "Then you see, *cara*, we do see eye-to-eye on two of the most important issues in your life. And if we can see eye-to-eye on these issues, I'm sure we'll agree on others."

She longed to clasp his hand, to hold it to her cheek forever. When he was gentle like this, when he was loving toward her, she felt so safe and so certain of her feelings.

He drew back, shoved his hands in his trouser pockets. "We should finish up with the contract. Get it signed and returned to Carl."

And suddenly she knew he was right. If anyone could protect the baby from Mark's selfishness and vindictive manipulations, it was Niccolo.

Meg took the documents from Nic and signed at

each of the indicated lines. Returning the pages to Nic, she felt almost immediate relief. For the first time in months she knew she'd done the right thing. Niccolo would do everything in his power for this—their—baby.

The wedding grew nearer. Between long hours spent working at the Hunts and Niccolo's many business appointments, she and Niccolo spent little time together. The first night she had dinner alone, Meg felt rather pleased. But quickly she discovered she truly missed his company.

She tried to tell herself she just felt lonely, but that wasn't it at all. Meg wasn't lonely. She simply wanted Nic. She liked the way he charged a room, making it feel brighter, warmer. She liked his laughter, the lines around his mouth, the glints in his eyes. She liked the way he said her name, the indulgence in his voice. He could be so hard, so unyielding, and yet he could also be tender and protective.

She missed him, missed being with him, and even if they weren't marrying for love, they were united in their desire to do what was best for the baby.

How could she not love a man who desperately wanted to do the right thing? Maybe morals weren't supposed to be sexy, but morals and Niccolo were beginning to drive her crazy.

Unusually restless, Meg wandered through the villa. She didn't want to work and wasn't interested in turning on the television. She could read, but that didn't really appeal, either.

She wanted to see Nic. Perhaps Francesca knew when he'd be back.

"He's in the tasting room." Francesca answered Meg's inquiry with a nod, and pointed her finger.

"He's meeting with someone?"

"No. He's just been having his dinner there." Francesca shrugged, focusing on the shopping list she'd been making. "If you're going there, will you take him his coffee for me?"

He'd been avoiding her, Meg realized, dismayed. He'd been dining alone, intentionally keeping his distance.

Meg balanced the cup and saucer as she walked down the back steps, across the terrace and past the tennis court to the tasting room.

She found him perched on a stool, studying a spreadsheet. He was dressed casually in jeans, work boots and a snug black T-shirt. He looked up as she closed the door, his eyes lighting, and then almost immediately the light died and his features hardened, losing all warmth.

She saw the change and felt it just as clearly inside her. "Your coffee," she said, nervously placing the cup and saucer in front of him. She didn't know why she suddenly felt jittery. She wished she didn't care so much about his feelings, but she did want him to like her. She did want him to enjoy being around her.

"You didn't have to do that. I could have come up to the house."

Something small and tight turned in her chest. "When? After I'd gone to bed?" She'd meant to sound flippant, instead she sounded hurt.

It was an idiotic thing to say. Emotional. Immature. "That didn't come out right. What I meant is that I've…missed you. Your company, I mean. And I just wanted to say hello.''

Grooves deepened on either side of his mouth. His smile looked strained. ''Hello.''

She felt like she'd swallowed a brick for dinner. ''Well, I guess that's that.'' She forced herself to sound cheerful and horrendously upbeat. ''Maybe I'll see you Saturday because, heavens, we're getting married then!''

She was babbling. She knew she was babbling, but she couldn't seem to stop herself. She let herself prattle on as she inched her way to the door.

It had been a mistake to come here tonight, a mistake to seek Niccolo out. She should have stayed in her room, minded her own business. Instead she'd deliberately put herself in his path, wanting him.

Wanting him.

Something tiny and electric surged through her, and from the look in Niccolo's eye, he saw it, too. Or he felt it, because suddenly he was on his feet and walking very slowly toward her.

''I was doing us a favor,'' he said, his voice deep, rich, softly accented. ''I thought it might help.''

''Help?'' she squeaked, drawing back a step, watching in silent fascination as he dragged the waistband of his T-shirt from his jeans.

''Something happens when we're alone together. You feel it. I feel it.''

''No.''

''Yes, and stop right there. Don't make me use my doggie commands with you tonight.'' Then he smiled at her, a real smile, with warmth and laughter glowing in his beautiful golden eyes. His smile made her feel as if they were sharing a private joke, and she loved the sweetness and the intimacy.

But Meg couldn't smile because her body quivered and her legs were turning to jelly.

"How brave are you, Maggie?" he whispered, drawing closer still.

"Not so brave," she answered in a breathless rush.

"Brave enough to play a little game?"

The gleam in his eye burned hotter and brighter. The gleam sent a frisson rippling through her belly. She touched the tip of her tongue to her upper lip. "What kind of game?"

"A children's game. One we used to play as kids."

"Truth or Dare?"

He nodded, eyebrows lifting. "Should I go first, or will you?"

Her mind scrambled, she searched for something to ask him. Suddenly she remembered Sonia, the actress, and Meg blushed even as she blurted her question. "Have you and Sonia Carlo ever been... intimate?"

"You didn't ask me, 'Truth or dare?' But I'll take the question." His mouth curved into a rueful smile. "No, I've never had sex with the lovely Miss Carlo. It's always been just an innocent flirtation."

He took a step toward her. "Truth or dare, *cara*?"

She swallowed hard. "Truth," she answered in a small voice.

"Why did you want to seduce me that night when you were in high school?"

"I—" she touched her tongue to her lip again. "I thought I loved you."

"You thought?" he asked, his expression puzzled,

perhaps even a little disappointed. But she wouldn't give him a chance to dwell on her answer.

Quickly, she asked, "Truth or dare, Niccolo?"

"Truth."

"When you threw me off your lap that night in the library—"

"When you were sixteen or just last week?"

"Last week," she answered breathlessly, struggling to finish the question before she turned chicken. "You looked so cool, so controlled. Did you really feel that way on the inside, or were you just putting on an act for me?"

He laughed softly. "You're asking very pointed questions."

"Truth, Nic."

"I wanted you, *cara*. I wanted you with every bone in my body, and then some." His lashes lowered, briefly fanning his cheek. "But Carl was scheduled to arrive, and I—"

"You what?"

"Was trying to make a point."

"Which was?"

"That I could make you want me just as much as I wanted you."

Warmth and excitement flooded her. She knew this was just a game, but she felt her heart race, her body deliciously awake.

"Truth or dare, *cara*?"

His voice sounded so silky. "Truth," she answered, suppressing a shudder.

"How many men have you been with?"

Heat burned her cheeks. "One," she answered, holding up her finger. "Just Mark."

He started to ask another question, but she cut him off. "My turn, Nic. Truth or dare?"

His golden eyes bored into her. "Dare."

The word came out harshly. She felt his tension, felt her own. Something was happening here, something that had nothing to do with playing a game.

"I dare you to take off your shirt," she whispered.

He drew his T-shirt over his head, leaving his sculpted shoulders and chest bare. She sucked in a breath at the sight of his smooth, taut, burnished skin. Slowly he dropped the shirt at his feet.

"Truth or dare, Maggie?"

"Dare."

"I dare you to come here, Maggie, and touch me."

She closed the remaining distance between them, lifted her hand but left it hovering in midair. "Where?" she breathed.

He took her hand, placed it on his chest. She felt his heart, the strong, fierce tempo, and still holding her hand, drew her palm down so she caressed the contoured muscles in his stomach and pelvis. "Your turn," he murmured, keeping her fingers flat against his taut belly.

His skin felt like satin over sinew. He was wonderful, strong, smooth. It was impossible for her to concentrate. "Truth or dare?" she breathed.

"Dare."

The huskiness in his voice was pure seduction. She pressed her fingertips against the firmness of his flesh, entranced by his beauty and warmth and playfulness. She'd never imagined that Niccolo could be like this.

"Come on, Maggie, give me a dare."

She lifted her head, gazed into his face. She wanted him. Wanted him. Wanted him.

"I dare you to make love to me."

CHAPTER NINE

THERE, the words were said. She couldn't take them back. Couldn't pretend they hadn't been spoken.

"Dare accepted." He captured her hands, lifting them above her head. "But I warn you, Maggie, you're going to have to wait a long long time for your turn, because this dare won't be rushed, and I won't be easily satisfied."

Excitement inspired a hint of panic. Maybe she should have suggested a different dare. Maybe she should have chosen something...safer. "Can I change my mind?"

"No." He backed her up one step at a time until her backbone bumped against the wall. Leaning past her, he shut the door. She couldn't help staring at him, fascinated by the play of light across his taut stomach, each muscle smoothly curved, light and shadows undulating across his smooth golden skin. He was all man, and beautiful. Her Niccolo. The man who'd stolen her heart so many years ago.

"There," he drawled, "that should give us some privacy."

Heat flooded her limbs. He made it sound wicked and wonderful at the same time. But just as suddenly she panicked. It was one thing to play a children's game. Quite another to make love on the winery's tasting room floor.

What if they did make love and he was disappointed? What if she really wasn't what he wanted? Meg didn't think she could bear another rejection.

Ducking beneath his arm, she tried to scramble for safety. But Nic moved just as quickly, and kneeling, he cornered her on the carpet.

"I thought you were brave," he said, crouching above her, trapping her body between his legs.

"No. Not anymore."

His teeth flashed, not quite a smile, and with humiliating ease, he dragged her lower so her hips lay just under his. The crush of the Berber carpet tickled her nape, pressed through her cotton top. "Then I'll have to teach you that, too."

Teach her that, too. A shiver danced up and down her spine.

"Hello, love," he drawled.

"Since when have I been your love?" And yet even as she said it, she felt a ripple of excitement, a craving for his strength and a taste of the sensual. She wanted to feel his mouth and his tongue, be driven wild by his hands, surrender to the rawness of her own desires

"I've never met a woman that likes to argue as much as you do," he said, lowering himself to his elbows, bracing himself just above her breasts.

The ripple within her widened, deepened. She shivered and he smiled faintly, aware of the tension in her rigid limbs, in her shallow breathing.

He kissed her mouth on a slant, his lips covering only a portion of hers. It was a maddening kiss, light, teasing, and when he kissed her again the same way, his tongue flicked the corner, tormenting her with the kiss's brevity.

She couldn't stand the teasing nature of the kiss.

Her mouth, her body, her senses screamed for more. Meg wound her arms around his neck, forcing his head lower, drawing his mouth to hers.

A hoarse sound came from Niccolo, primitive and raw. His arms tightened, and a knee slid between her legs, parting them as he kissed her in earnest, his tongue stroking her upper lip. As her legs parted to accept his strength, her mouth opened to him with a soft, strangled sigh.

Nic's body hardened against her, his arousal thrusting against her still flat abdomen, and she melted from the inside out. The evidence of his desire thrilled her. His arousal fueled her own. Lifting her hips, she blindly sought more contact.

Briefly his head lifted, and Meg murmured an urgent protest. Niccolo smiled faintly, kissing the side of her mouth and then her chin. "You look so disappointed."

She didn't have to say anything. He knew. His kisses dropped lower, his mouth moving to the curve of her breast. She throbbed inwardly, muscles clenching, blood pooling. His teeth closed around one exquisitely erect nipple, and she gasped.

Nic suckled her breast through the fabric of her blouse. Brilliant light exploded inside her head even as the core of her ached, wanting more, needing more.

"You've turned my world upside down," he whispered against her mouth. "I'm confused, Maggie. I don't know what to feel anymore."

It crossed her mind that this would be a good time to pull back and regain some control. If ever two people needed to talk, it was them. But Meg had waited so long to be in his arms, to feel him against her, that she ignored the voice of reason and curved herself against him, thigh to thigh, hip to hip, breast to chest. The loneliness of the last five months, the emptiness of her dating relationships, the separation from her parents seemed to ball inside her, combining to form a great, consuming need.

She needed Nic. She needed his love. Not on their wedding day, but right now.

"Are we still playing the game?" she whispered, blood pounding, body pulsating, her limbs liquid with need.

Niccolo lifted his head and gazed deep into her eyes. His breath was ragged. "We're past games, Maggie. This is just you and me."

It was the answer she wanted, the answer she hoped to hear. *Just you and me.*

Niccolo didn't have to love her, at least not yet, but of course someday she hoped he would. But for now, if he knew who she was, if he wanted her for herself, then making love was right, and very real.

His hand slid to the waistband of her gabardine slacks, unfastened the button and opened the zipper. The cool air against her bare skin made her muscles contract, followed immediately by the slow caress of Niccolo's hand.

She shuddered as he cupped her hipbone, his fingers like a rain of fire on her bare tummy. He found the apex of her thighs and brushed the curls protecting her sex. Her body trembled, her inner thighs clenching. With delicious intent, Nic parted her thighs to trace her most delicate skin, discovering her heat and eager dampness.

Meg reached for him, impatient with his jeans, wanting to feel the smooth polish of his skin. As she tugged at the buttons on his jeans, she heard voices outside the winery window. Stiffening, Meg looked at Nic. Nic sat up, pulled her to a sitting position.

The door swung open even as they scrambled to cover themselves, but Meg's fingers felt numb, and Niccolo smoothed her blouse and dragged his fingers through her chaotic curls.

"Maggie? Niccolo?"

God, her parents! They'd returned early from their trip.

As Francesca served plates of fruit and cheese, Niccolo's golden gaze sought Meg's over the rim of his espresso cup. She knew her cheeks still glowed, and desire clouded her brain, making it hard for her to think.

"We couldn't stay away," Meg's mother was saying, smiling her thanks at Francesca before turning her attention to the young couple. "Once we'd received Nic's telegram, the cruise lost its luster. I'm hoping there's something I can do to help, some little detail needing handling."

"Most things have been settled, but you're right, Eileen," Nic said, nodding, "there are always small things that get overlooked until the last minute."

They talked at length about the wedding, Niccolo unusually animated as he shared with her parents the wedding plans. He'd hired a string quartet for the cocktail hour and a fabulous dance band for dinner. A dozen uniformed wait staff would pass the trays of appetizers before serving the five-course seated dinner.

"You're spending a fortune, son," John Buckner said quietly, shifting in his armchair. "Traditionally, it's the bride's family's responsibility to foot the bill—''

''I want to do this,'' Nic interrupted gently but firmly. ''It's my gift to Maggie. It's important to me.''

In the end her father caved in. Meg was glad to know she wasn't the only one who couldn't say no to Niccolo.

Francesca appeared in the doorway, signaling to Nic, letting him know he'd received a call. Nic excused himself, and Meg and her parents discussed the wedding plans yet again.

Niccolo returned twenty minutes later, and Meg immediately sensed something had happened to change his mood. Just a half hour earlier he'd been nearly ebullient as he discussed the wedding. Now he listened, utterly detached, his expression shuttered, his words, when he did speak, terse.

By the time her parents left, it was well past midnight. Niccolo silently walked with Meg up the staircase, and she struggled to think of something to say. Hard to believe that this cold, distant man was the same one who'd almost made love to her hours earlier on the winery floor.

As she paused outside her bedroom door, she wished he'd take her in his arms again, display just a little of the warmth and affection he'd shown her earlier.

Instead he held himself stiffly, making a point of keeping his distance. ''If I don't see you in the morning, we'll meet for dinner. Don't forget we've invited your parents to join us.''

''I won't.''

''I'll leave it to you to settle the arrangements with

Francesca. You should be taking that responsibility over, anyway. Just let her know the number of guests, the time dinner is planned and the menu you'd like served. Francesca will take care of the rest.''

Meg nodded, feeling the gulf widen between them. She wondered yet again what had happened to change his mood. He'd been fine until he'd left to take the call. It couldn't have anything to do with her, could it? It wouldn't be Mark.... -

No. That was ridiculous. It was a winery problem. Something to do with business.

Niccolo's mood was much improved by the next evening. He wasn't exactly talkative during dinner, but he listened closely and smiled at the anecdotes her mother shared.

''Sounds like a good trip,'' he said, filling her mother's wineglass before passing the bottle to her father. ''I hope Maggie and I will enjoy our honeymoon half as much.''

Honeymoon! Meg sat up straighter. This was news to her.

''My family owns a small private island off the coast of Naples. It's been in the family nearly a half century. A simple place, but there's something about the light and intensely blue water that makes it dazzling this time of year.''

Honeymoon, she repeated silently, unable to think of anything but lovemaking. Finally, she and Nic would be alone together. Finally she'd know him in every sense of the word.

''You haven't said a word, Maggie,'' her father said.

"She's just overwhelmed. Brides usually are," her mother replied. "I remember how nervous I felt," she added with an affectionate smile at her husband, then Meg. "I could hardly eat or sleep the last couple days, so much in love."

"Yes," Nic drawled, leaning back in his chair, grooves deepening alongside his mouth. "So much like our Maggie."

Perhaps the others didn't catch his cynical tone, but Meg did, and she held her breath for a moment, surprised by the sarcasm. What was bothering him?

Was he having second thoughts about the ceremony? New regrets? Well, it wasn't too late to cancel the ceremony. All he had to do was speak up!

"Nic, I want you to know that Eileen and I couldn't be happier about this wedding." John Buckner sat forward, broad tanned forearms resting against the table's edge. "You've always been like a son—" his voice broke on the word *son,* and for a second he struggled to find his voice "—to us. I know you're also expecting a baby early next year, and I want to thank you for doing the right thing."

The right thing. The exact thing Niccolo had said. Her dad and Nic were more alike than they knew.

Nic's golden eyes met hers, and he regarded her steadily. Suddenly she realized they were all looking at her, waiting for her to speak. "Nic's been wonderful," she said in a strangled voice.

"I have to admit, I was a little surprised at first," her father added. "Nic didn't strike me as the kind of man to not take precautions, but as your mom said to me, mistakes happen, and now that I've gotten used to the idea of a baby, I'm looking forward to being a grandpa. We haven't had a little tyke around the place in years. Not since you and Jared..." His voice drifted off and again he struggled for words, this time unable to finish the thought.

Pain seemed to radiate from her dad. His broad shoulders slumped, his body almost doubling with the grief he'd never come to grips with. Guilt assailed Meg.

Leaning forward, she touched her father's muscular forearm. Even at sixty-two, he had the rugged build of a rancher, the lean strength of a man who'd spent most of his life working the land, yet his grief was almost more than he could bear. "I'm sorry, Dad."

His fingers closed over hers.

"Please forgive me," she whispered.

His shoulders shifted, and slowly he lifted his head. His blue eyes, the same vivid blue as Meg's, met hers. "You didn't mean any harm that night," he said quietly, and yet his voice broke, reminding her of his still broken heart.

"Daddy, I'd do anything to bring Jared back. I would."

Almost gingerly he touched the back of her head and then her cheek. His deep voice shook. "I know."

She gripped his hand tightly. "I loved him, too."

Meg didn't see the frustration in Nic's eyes, nor the grief in her mother's.

Abruptly, Niccolo stood. "This isn't right," he rasped, his complexion pale, his jaw jutting forward. "I can't let Maggie continue doing this—"

"Nic, *no*." Meg struggled to her feet, trying to put distance between Nic and her parents.

"Maggie's not at fault," he said, ignoring her.

She caught his shirt sleeve. "You promised me," she whispered desperately. "You *promised*."

"I was wrong to promise," he retorted grimly.

Her father pushed back his chair. "What do you mean, Nic? What's this about?"

Nic stared into her face for a moment, his gaze searching hers, before pulling free. He turned to face her father. "Jared and I were drinking that night. Drinking pretty heavily." He shot a quick glance at her before continuing. "Maggie took the keys because we were in no condition to drive. She was trying to protect Jared. Trying to do what you'd want her to do."

The dining room was utterly silent when he finished speaking. No one moved. No one spoke. The only sound was the soft pop of an ice cube as it melted in one of the crystal goblets.

Her father picked up a fork. He stared at the bright, polished silver tines, fingers clenched around the handle.

Meg's heart beat wildly.

He set the fork down, the silver making a ping as it bumped a china dessert plate. "Why didn't you say something before?"

Niccolo smiled bitterly. "Because I was a coward."

Tears filled Meg's eyes. "No, Nic—"

"Yes," he interrupted harshly. "For years I've let you blame Maggie, and I'm ashamed of myself, ashamed of my immaturity and selfishness. Maggie should never have been blamed for the accident. If anyone's at fault, it's me. I was the oldest. I'm responsible."

In that moment, she fell in love with him all over

again. What he was doing was painful for him, for all of them, and yet he was determined to right a wrong.

John Buckner looked at his wife and then at his daughter. His blue eyes were puzzled, his voice rough with emotion. "Why didn't you tell us, Maggie?"

Her stomach cramped. "I couldn't. I…" Her gaze clung to her father's, begging him to understand. "I know how much you loved Jared."

His vivid blue eyes filmed, the tears turning the brilliant blue to aquamarine. "No more than I love you," he replied hoarsely. "Never more than I loved you."

Wrung out, Meg showered, changed into her striped nightshirt and fell into bed. But sleep eluded her. Her mind raced, and her emotions felt dangerously out of control.

An hour after turning out her light, Meg heard footsteps on the stairs. Niccolo was still awake. Hurrying to her door, she glimpsed him heading down the darkened hall to his suite of rooms.

"Nic!"

Her whisper carried, and he turned.

Slowly he walked the length of the hall. "What's wrong?"

"I can't sleep."

"Too much in love?" he drawled, a black eyebrow rising.

He sounded as if he hated her, and yet she saw something else in his face, pain and tenderness. He might not yet know it, but he needed her as much as she needed him. Wordlessly she took his hand in hers and drew him into her dark bedroom. "Stay with me," she whispered, softly closing the door behind her.

"I don't understand."

"Yes, you do. Stay with me tonight. Let's finish what we started."

"The game?"

She couldn't read his expression in the dark. Couldn't see more than the shadows of his face, the brief flash of his teeth. "Why not?"

"You dared me to make love to you."

"I did." Her voice dropped, her inflection deepening.

She felt his hands slide across her shoulders, fingers grazing her shoulder blades then meeting at the back of her neck. He drew small, slow circles on her nape before dragging his hands into her hair. His fingers twined in her long curls, imprisoning her. His mouth descended, and he kissed her with bottled emotion, his lips crushing hers, parting hers, his tongue probing the inside of her mouth, demanding a response.

Her body gave in to him. She curved to meet him, soft where he was hard, warm where he was rigid. Instinctively she knew this was what they needed. Skin, sinew, strength. Already there had been too many words spoken.

He carried her to the bed and dragged her cotton nightshirt over her head. Cupping her full breasts, he suckled one nipple and then the other. She moaned, arched against him, her hands grappling with his belt and the shirt tucked into his trousers.

He helped her undress him and then his hard naked body stretched against her, a knee parting her thighs, a hand moving across the soft swell of her belly to her intimate warmth. She was damp, soft and ready. She wanted him inside her, a finger, his penis, *him*, but he wouldn't give her the satisfaction.

Her legs parted wider, and she slid her hand down his strong torso to his lean hips. She grasped him in her hand, stroking him with the urgency she felt building within her.

The ache was almost intolerable. She needed his heat and length, needed to be filled by him. She caught his face, kissed his lips, breathing him in. He smelled of oranges and spice, of moonlight and wine. No one but Niccolo could smell so divine.

He drew her hands from his face and kissed the length of her, discovering erogenous zones she didn't even know existed. Ear, base of throat, the hollow under her arm, the curve beneath her breast. By the time he reached her inner thighs she was a trembling mess.

He kissed between her thighs, his tongue tracing her delicate lines and her warm, damp core. She pressed against his head, begging him to stop, wanting him to enter her instead. Yet he wouldn't back off, his tongue playing against her bud and then thrusting at her dampness.

She couldn't control the frantic tension building within her body, the coiling, tight and sweet, making her fingernails dig into his shoulders. Her legs buckled at the knees, and the sole of a foot arched against the tangled sheet.

"Please, Nic," she gasped, and he suddenly pulled himself up, kneeling between her quivering thighs.

"Will this hurt you?" he whispered roughly.

"No."

"And the baby?"

"No. He'll be fine."

Without another word, he drove himself into her, answering the empty ache inside her body. He filled her, covered her body with his, his groan so soft she almost didn't hear it.

Nic's hands clasped hers, his fingers pressing between hers, and he slid her arms above her head until his chest stretched taut, nipples grazing her swollen, aching peaks. Slowly he thrust into her, extending his body, driving deep, and then he withdrew only to thrust hard again. Then, as her hips began lifting to meet his body, he moved faster, his thrusts coming faster, his hips rocking deeply into her.

It was the most exquisite sensation she'd ever felt. She felt hot and raw and primal and she wanted even more. She wanted him harder and faster until she couldn't think another thought.

The quiver inside her body quickened, sharp, silver desire turning in on itself, balling into something bigger, hotter, brighter. She felt more alive than she'd ever felt before, and as Niccolo thrust, she arched against him, hands pressing against his weight. Suddenly she was no longer in control of herself. Her body controlled her.

She knew what an orgasm was. She thought she'd had one before, but that—that was nothing like this explosion of mind and body and senses. As she writhed in Nic's arms, she heard his guttural groan, and with a last, fierce thrust, he strained against her, drawing her to him as if he was afraid she'd disappear.

Breathing raggedly, still buried within her, he shifted them to the side. Reaching out, he brushed a dark curl from her damp cheek, tucking it behind her ear. Aftershocks coursed through her, ripple after ripple, and Niccolo kissed her swollen, sensitive mouth. "Do you know what we've just done?"

Her mouth felt dry, her body boneless. "Made love."

"No. I've made you mine," he answered, cupping one of her breasts, letting the weight of it rest in his callused palm. "There will never be anyone else."

He kissed her jaw, her chin, the base of her neck. His tongue flicked across her distended nipple, his breath warm, her skin tingling. "Soon I shall have you every which way I want you. You will be my wife. You will belong to me. No one but me."

Dazed by the intensity in his voice and the erotic warmth of his mouth on her breast, she couldn't protest.

"Tell me you understand," he commanded.

She felt his fingers drag through her hair, fanning her curls behind her head. "I understand."

She couldn't see his face, but she felt his fierceness, his muscles taut. "Who was your first, Maggie? Who took away your innocence?"

"Don't do this, Niccolo."

"Answer me."

Sighing, she kissed his shoulder, her lips moving across the smooth bundle of muscle. "You would have been."

"I should have been," he answered darkly, thumbs sweeping over her cheekbones like a sculptor examining his work of art. He kissed her again, this time with a softness she didn't expect, tenderness and hunger in the quest of his tongue, in the pressure of his hands as they molded her to him.

"You must promise me something."

"What?"

He pushed another curl from her warm, flushed face. "Promise me you'll never see Mark again, nor will you ever have contact of any kind with him."

"Nic, he's not a threat—"

"That's not the point. He's part of the past. I don't want to fight with his ghost. I want you to choose me."

"And I do!"

"Then promise me you'll have no contact with him. I need to trust you, Maggie. I need to know you trust me. Do you understand?"

"Yes."

He flipped her onto her back and kissed her once more, his tongue sliding across the inside of her lower lip. Helplessly she arched against him, hands caressing his broad, solid chest. She felt the ache start up, the desire coiling tighter than before. How could she want him so soon?

They made love again, this time more frantic, their hands and mouths and bodies searching. Meg felt as if she'd waited her entire life to be close to Niccolo, and she couldn't get enough.

He drove her to another shattering climax, his orgasm beginning at the end of hers, and Meg held him as he bucked with the intensity of it. He cried out her name as he came, and Meg had to bite her lip to keep from whispering she loved him.

They collapsed together, Meg falling asleep still wrapped in Nic's arms. She slept deeply, dreamlessly, until she woke and discovered her drapes drawn and sunlight pouring through the tall arched windows.

Saturday morning, her wedding day.

CHAPTER TEN

THE wedding, planned as it was at the last moment, came off flawlessly.

Meg had never seen anyone half so dashing as Niccolo in his elegant tuxedo. The sharp collar on the white shirt, the black bow tie, the lapel on the tuxedo highlighted his beautiful cheekbones and perfect mouth.

That mouth that kissed her senseless made her yearn for the sun and the moon and the stars. She loved his mouth. Loved him.

Last-minute jitters made her press her bouquet against her straight white skirt. The long silk sheath fit snugly, so snugly that Meg was afraid she wouldn't be able to walk, much less sit down. But the stylist the salon sent with the dress performed a miraculous conversion, opening a small hidden seam in the back and hooking an overskirt in a dove gray satin on her hips. Meg loved the gray overskirt against the white silk. With the Dominici jewels sparkling in her dark hair, left long and loose per Niccolo's request, she truly felt like a bride, a bride very much in love, a bride anxious to marry the man of her dreams.

They said their vows in the small stone chapel on the edge of the winery property. The chapel had been built in memory of Niccolo's grandfather, and when the Dominici family visited Napa, it was there they held their family services.

Meg gazed into Niccolo's golden eyes, and her voice was firm as she promised to love, honor and obey him. But as she said *obey* Nic's black eyebrows lifted, his lovely mouth quirked, and she felt a frisson of feeling. This was almost too incredible.

But more than anything, she wanted the marriage to work, and she was determined to make Nic proud of her. He might not love her romantically, but he did care about her, and he was attracted to her physically. That much she had discovered last night. All they needed was time to settle in together and the opportunity to become a real family.

The orchestra played until the early hours of the morning. The guests dined and danced, dined and danced yet again. The tiered wedding cake tasted even better than it looked, and everyone cheered when Niccolo slid the garter off Meg's slim thigh and tossed it to the eligible bachelors crowding close.

Meg was gratified by Nic's attention. He didn't let her out of his sight for more than five minutes the entire evening, clasping her hand in his as they made the rounds of the tables, visiting with each of the guests, accepting congratulations and kissing after appropriate toasts.

The evening was so perfect she almost believed they were really in love.

Almost, that is, except for the snugness of her gown at her waist, and the strange little flutter she felt in her abdomen. It was like the wings of a butterfly, a brief tickle inside her skin.

Covering her stomach with her hand, she looked at Nic in surprise.

"What's wrong, Maggie?" he asked, lowering his head to her ear. "Are you not feeling well?"

"I'm fine."

"Then what is it?"

"It's the baby. I felt him." She smiled, delighted and shocked and on the verge of tears. "He moved!"

Nic tilted her chin up and pressed his mouth to hers. His kiss was infinitely tender. "I think he's giving his approval," he murmured. "We've done the right thing, Maggie. We're doing what's best for our son."

But she needed reassurance, and reaching up, she touched his face, feeling the warmth of his skin and the hard curve of his cheekbone. "Are you happy?"

"Yes." He turned his face, kissed her palm. "I know we've done the right thing, and that makes me happy."

Not that he was happy about marrying her, but that he was happy about doing the right thing.

It hurt her pride, but there wasn't much she could do. She knew the terms at the outset. Niccolo was Niccolo. She could not change him. She could only hope his feelings for her would grow, and grow quickly. Just like the baby.

At midnight they boarded Niccolo's private jet at the business airport in Santa Rosa. Although Niccolo frequently flew his own planes, he'd handed controls over to one of his commercial pilots for the all-night flight.

They arrived on the small private island before noon. Meg slept most of the way, curled into her leather fold-out chair, although Nic indicated she was welcome to use the tiny private bedroom at the back.

Meg showered at the villa, changing from her traveling suit into a long sarong skirt and matching lightweight top in her favorite color, periwinkle blue. She started to pin her hair up before remembering how much Niccolo liked it loose. She let it drop, the rich curls cascading down her back. After all, it was her honeymoon.

Downstairs, Nic met her on the massive columned veranda. He handed her a bubbly orange juice. ''Don't worry,'' he said, ''no alcohol. It's just seltzer water.''

He escorted her to lunch, and they sat in a gorgeous pagoda made of glass with a breathtaking view of Naples and the surrounding coast. ''This must be heaven,'' she said, awed by the startling turquoise water, perfect azure sky, verdant green and lemon yellow of the villa.

She knew the Dominici family was wealthy, but the sheer opulence of the Italian villa left her speechless. This was extravagance on a scale she'd never known.

He smiled faintly, enjoying her wonder. ''No, *cara*, heaven is what's going to happen later.'' His husky inflection left her in no doubt of his meaning.

She felt a blush sweep her face, turning her cheeks pink. He made her want things no nice girl should want, and the very intensity of her longing made her sidestep the issue. ''Will we see any of your family while we're here? They didn't make it to the wedding, and it's been years since I've seen any of them.''

''I was disappointed they couldn't come, but it was short notice,'' he answered, pouring more of the bubbly juice into her glass.

''And we won't be going to Florence this trip?''

"Unfortunately, no. My father has business plans, and Mother is busy with her fashions and parties."

She didn't want to make an issue of it, but she couldn't let the subject drop, either. "They know, don't they, about us?"

"Yes, of course."

She didn't know why she couldn't drop it. The fact that they might be upset about the wedding was a new and unpleasant thought. "They're pleased, aren't they?"

His golden gaze met hers, his lips curving ruefully. "It's a bit of a surprise, Maggie. But they'll adjust. They know how close we once were."

They finished their meal in near silence. Over coffee Niccolo reached for her hand and drew her fingers to his mouth. He pressed a kiss to her fingertips, and then another to her palm. "Don't look so sad. This is our honeymoon, *cara*."

"I know. But I feel selfish. I've been so caught up in all the wedding plans, and my feelings, that I didn't ever stop to think about your family."

"My brother is thrilled. You met him once. Remember how well we all got along?" She nodded. Nic continued, "And my parents, well, truthfully, they wanted a big society wedding for their youngest son, but they don't dislike you. How could they? I chose you for my wife."

He made it sound so simple. She tried to smile, wondering why she suddenly felt like weeping. It had to be the pregnancy making her teary.

He sucked the tip of her finger, his mouth and tongue wakening the hunger inside her. "Now if you're done eating, there's something I'm dying to taste again."

*   *   *

She couldn't count the number of times they made love that week. The days and nights blurred into an intoxicating cocoon of sensual pleasure. He kissed every inch of her body, made love to her with his lips, tongue, hands. He stripped her of her remaining inhibitions, unleashing a passion she'd always kept buried.

"You're so incredibly beautiful," he murmured, his voice husky. It was their last night on the island, and they'd spent hours in bed, curtains open to capture the ocean breeze and the distant lights dotting the coastline.

Slowly he traced her soft, swollen mouth with a fingertip. "Just the curve of your lip promises pleasure. It is a perfect mouth, a mouth for love, a mouth for sex."

Then he kissed her again, this time with a bittersweet hunger that brought tears to her eyes.

"I don't want to go back," she whispered, holding him tightly, afraid to let go. "Can't we stay here forever?"

He drew his fingers through her hair, untangling the long, dark curls. "You'd grow tired of me, *cara*. You're easily bored."

Her heart tightened in a spasm of pain. How could he say such a thing?

She'd loved him since she was twelve, when she was a girl, skinny and fearless in braids and denim overalls. Back then Niccolo Dominici was her brother's new friend, a handsome dark teenager visiting from Florence. An Italian boy-man with eyes like gold and a smile that made her feel funny on the inside, empty and yearning, and she hadn't understood the longing, or the desperate emotion.

Tears filled her eyes. She pressed her knuckled fists against the smooth, warm skin of his back, needing him as if she were a drowning woman hanging on to a life preserver.

As if Nic felt her love and longing, he clasped her head, holding her close, without words.

It was, she thought, her heart in her throat, the happiest she'd ever been, and yet she knew better than anyone that happiness was fleeting.

On the flight to the States, Niccolo announced they'd be stopping in New York for a day. He had a meeting with Dominici family members living on the East Coast, and he thought Maggie should be there when the movers arrived to pack her apartment and send everything to their Napa Valley home.

Shyly, Meg let Nic into her small apartment. She hadn't been home in three weeks, and her plants were wilted on the terrace. Mail lay in front of the door, and the red light on her answering machine indicated she'd received twenty-three messages.

The moving company was scheduled to arrive in half an hour. Meg bit her lip as she glanced around her small but snug apartment. It might have been better if she hadn't returned. She'd never been very good at leaving or saying goodbye.

As if he could read her mind, Niccolo enfolded her in his strong arms. "It's all right," he said, kissing her upturned face. "Your things will find a new home. It'll be an adjustment for both of us, but soon you'll be settled in."

"You're right, of course. I've just grown attached to the city. I love the secret gardens and the energy of Manhattan."

"Then perhaps we should buy a place here."

She took a step back. "That'd be too expensive!"

"Maggie, I have plenty of money. Don't you worry about the finances." He chuckled softly, kissed the top of her head. "Actually, it's a good idea. Your design firm is headquartered here. They've already told you that they'll need you here for monthly meetings, and I frequently make trips to the East Coast."

"Wouldn't a hotel be cheaper?"

"Not if we're traveling with the baby. He'll want space to play. Which reminds me, when we get back to Napa you see about getting the nursery done. It's never too soon to have everything ready."

The movers arrived. Just before leaving, Niccolo reminded her that his meeting would go late, but he hoped to join her at the Ritz-Carlton for dinner by eight-thirty, nine at the latest. Then he kissed her and excused himself, aware that his limousine waited downstairs, ready to whisk him to his meeting in Connecticut.

"Well, well, Margaret. You're moving up in the world, aren't you?"

Meg stiffened at the sound of the voice. *Mark.*

Revulsion coursed through her as she turned toward the doorway. The movers had been carrying boxes and furniture up and down and had propped the front door open. "What are you doing here?"

"Your building manager said you'd be moving out today. Lucky I caught you before you left."

"Get out, before I call the police." She made the threat before she remembered the phone, along with nearly everything else, had already been packed.

"Don't get all excited. I'm not here to fight. I'm sick of fighting. That's all I ever do with my wife anymore." He stumbled to the plastic-wrapped couch and sat down heavily, covering his face with his hands. "God, my life's a mess!"

She refused to feel sorry for him. "That's your doing, Mark."

"I know. I know. You don't need to remind me." He rubbed his face with his hands, like a kid in desperate need of sleep. "My wife's talking about a divorce."

"I don't blame her!"

He looked at her over the tips of his fingers. "We have three kids together. Three great kids. They don't deserve to go through this."

Her chest tightened. She did feel badly for the children. Then she remembered her baby, remembered how he'd tried to strike a bargain with Nic. "Why did you ask Niccolo for money?"

Mark shrugged. "I'm broke."

"You're not. You drive expensive cars, live in the swankiest neighborhood—"

"All on credit." He smiled thinly. "Margaret, I'm in the hole so deep I don't see light anymore. I haven't made money in years. Oh, I go to work, but I'm scared to death to trade. A trader who doesn't trade loses his accounts. Mine dried up ages ago."

"Your wife doesn't know?"

He shook his head, a rueful expression shaping his features. "She likes living in the lap of luxury, and so I let her spend."

Meg slowly sat on a chair opposite him. "What were you doing with me, Mark?"

He rubbed his hands together and looked at her

from beneath his lashes. "Escaping." When she didn't answer he added, "When I was with you I forgot my problems for awhile. You're so beautiful and so...alive. When we were together I felt almost like a man again."

She hadn't wanted to care about his problems, hadn't meant to feel anything but anger and disgust, yet his despair moved her. She couldn't imagine living with so much unhappiness. "You are a man," she said gently.

"Not if we lose our home," he said, still rubbing his hands.

"You're behind in mortgage payments?"

"Six months. They gave me until this Friday to come up with the money. But I don't have that kind of money. And no one is going to give me a loan." He glanced at Meg, his eyes red-rimmed. "Heck, I wouldn't give myself a loan."

Meg smiled even as hot tears scalded the backs of her eyes. "Maybe Nic can help you again."

Mark shook his head. "I already asked him."

"When?"

"Two weeks ago Thursday. I called in the evening, asking if he'd perhaps extend me some more credit." Mark winced. "Actually, I begged, but Mr. Dominici still said no."

"How much do you need?"

He named a sum that made her gasp. What had he done with Nic's original payoff?

"I know." He turned dark red. "It's a small fortune."

It was a small fortune. It was everything in her checking and her savings accounts combined.

She looked at Mark, then at the huge diamond and

sapphire ring Nic had placed on her finger during the wedding.

She'd never want for anything again. She knew Nic. He'd always provide for her and the baby.

But Mark's children. His *other* children…

Her hand shook as she reached into her purse and withdrew her checkbook. Niccolo wouldn't approve of her doing this. But she wasn't doing this for Nic. She was doing it for her baby, for the half brothers and sister her baby would never know.

She handed him a check. "I hope this helps."

He stared at her so long and hard that she felt a lump grow in her throat. His red-rimmed eyes blinked. His mouth worked. He cleared his throat, the sound raw and hoarse. "Thank you."

"You're welcome," she answered gently, and she meant it.

After Mark left, Meg panicked. What had she done?

What hadn't she done?

She'd emptied her savings, broken her promise to Nic and given money to Mark. Nic would be furious.

She'd have to tell him. She just didn't know how.

Sick with anxiety, Meg paced the suite at the Ritz-Carlton, her high heels sinking into the plush carpeting. She'd dressed for dinner but knew she'd never manage to eat.

Niccolo unlocked the door to their suite at five minutes before nine. His gaze swept her figure, resting possessively on her figure before returning to her pale, composed face. "You look beautiful."

She was wearing an off-white wool swing coat and a short slim skirt, pale hose and taupe-colored heels. The skirt showed off her legs. The swing coat hid the swell of her tummy. Despite the designer labels in her clothes, she felt hideously naked.

"Thank you." A lump formed in her throat.

"Anywhere special you'd like to go for dinner?"

"Back to the island?"

He missed the thread of desperation in her voice. Smiling, he shrugged off his overcoat, dropped it on a chair. "I wish we could."

She felt her eyes burn, her throat close. She couldn't cry. Couldn't break down in front of him. Fighting for control, she grasped at the first thing that came to mind. "How did your meeting go?"

"So-so," he answered, looking more weary than she'd seen him in days. "Family business isn't always good business. It's hard not to step on each other's toes."

Of that she was sure.

He walked to the elegant suite bar, poured himself a drink. "Want one?"

"I wish."

"Sorry." He opened a chilled bottle of mineral water for her, carried the drinks to where she stood at the window.

He handed her the glass. As he lowered his head to kiss her, she noted the fine lines fanning from his eyes and the strain etched near his mouth. His lips brushed the side of her neck. "I missed you today."

He sounded almost apologetic, as if he'd admitted to a weakness. "There's a tragedy." She attempted to sound teasing.

He answered by taking her in one arm, drawing her firmly against him. He cupped her bottom with his palm. She felt his strength, and something else.

"You're shameless," she told him, standing on

tiptoe, kissing his chin. "Sex, sex, sex. That's all you ever think about anymore."

"Not true. I think about you."

If only that were true!

Suddenly she knew she couldn't tell him about Mark's visit. He didn't have to know. It wasn't as if Nic needed to be bothered with it. It was her money. Her decision. She didn't have to explain anything.

Nic tilted her face to his and kissed her, his lips firm, warm, searching. "Let me just check messages and then we'll head out."

Nic listened, then snapped his cell phone shut. Slowly he turned to look at Meg. His features were contorted, his lip curling in disgust. She waited for him to speak, but he didn't. He simply stared at her through narrowed lashes.

"Bad news?" she whispered.

"Your bank called."

Her heart slammed into her ribs.

"It seems the check you wrote to Mark didn't clear. But the bank honored it anyway, as a courtesy to me." Nic made a rude, rough sound in the back of his throat. "I don't know who's a bigger fool. You or me."

He was crushing her heart in his hand. "Nic, don't say that."

He turned away, dragging a hand through his thick, inky hair. "Where did you meet him?"

"I didn't *meet* him anywhere. He showed up at the apartment this afternoon. I asked him to go…"

"But he wouldn't. He got rough. Made threats."

"No."

"But you gave him money."

Her stomach heaved. "He's broke. His family could lose their house."

"I know. He came to me again, shortly after he signed the adoption papers. I told him under no circumstance would he receive another penny from me."

"He told me that, too."

Nic's head shot around. The look he gave her was one of disbelief. "But you wrote him a check anyway?"

She didn't answer.

Swearing softly, Nic poured himself another drink, downed it with a single flick of his wrist. "I told you to let me handle this, and you promised me you would. You agreed that there'd be no contact. Maggie, you gave me your *word*."

"Nic, you don't understand what it's like to be poor. Mark's drowning in debt. His wife is about to leave him. The children—our child's half siblings—need a place to live—"

"Don't tell me you feel sorry for the bastard!"

She swallowed hard. "He needed help. Someone had to help him."

"But not you! Not *my wife*."

"It's just money, Nic."

Nic slammed his glass down, the ice cubes clinking. "You don't get it, do you? This isn't about money. It's about trust. And commitment. You made a promise to me but you had no intention of keeping it."

"That's not fair!"

"It's more than fair. It's dead-on." He swore softly, ruffled his dark hair. His golden gaze skimmed her before dismissing her with a low, bitter laugh. "My God, you've turned my life inside out."

"I won't give him more money."

"No, you won't, because you won't see him ever again, and I'll make sure you have no more contact with him, even if I have to keep you at the villa under lock and key."

CHAPTER ELEVEN

NIC didn't speak to her on the thirty-minute drive to the airport. He read a business newspaper and looked over correspondence.

The Fokker jet was waiting at the airport. The pilot stepped out, shook Nic's hand, greeted Meg and took their luggage from them, stowing it in the back of the sleek white-and-burgundy-striped jet.

Twenty minutes later they were in the air, and Niccolo again immersed himself in paperwork, running numbers on his calculator, working on his laptop computer, everything but acknowledging her.

Meg closed her magazine an hour into the flight, unable to concentrate on the glossy celebrity photos when she felt so disturbed. She slipped the magazine into the side pocket on the leather lounge chair and looked across the mahogany table where Nic sat working, head bent, black hair gleaming in the overhead light. "Can we please talk?" she murmured.

"I've got work to do."

"It's midnight, Nic."

"If you're bored, sleep. I've got a company to run, a family up in arms, and grapes suffering from a new root fungus. I don't have time to baby-sit."

Blood rushed to her cheeks. "Baby-sit?"

He lifted his head, just barely, his contemptuous gaze meeting hers. "You're like a little child that must constantly be minded. Frankly, it bores me."

His words hit her like two humiliating slaps. Right.

Left. She gripped the arms of the lounge chair, fiercely fighting tears. How could he change from tender lover to arrogant brute in less than three hours? "Nic, I know you don't understand why I felt compelled to help him, but I did, and I don't regret my decision."

"Even now, knowing how angry I am, you'd do it again?"

His glittering gaze held her. "Yes," she whispered, her heart thumping painfully.

"My God, how could I even think this would be a real marriage, much less a real relationship?"

"You're blowing this out of proportion!"

"Maggie, this man, this married man, got you pregnant and then pressured you to abort the baby. When I approached him about adopting the baby, he demanded money. Less than two days after receiving a fortune, he calls me again, wheedling for more. He's a pathetic excuse for a man—"

"Maybe," she interrupted hotly, "but I won't kick him while he's down!"

"No, you'll just support his corrupt life-style." He stared at her long and hard, his features rigid, like a mask. "I did not marry you so you could indulge your lover and squander our financial resources. In case you didn't understand it before, when you married me, you pledged to love, honor and obey. I would say you've already failed on all three counts."

Stunned by his vindictive diatribe, she could barely find her voice. "You make me want to hate you."

"Good. It'll help keep things simple."

Her mouth was dry, her throat as parched as if

she'd swallowed cotton. "Our honeymoon was beautiful. Why are you ruining it now?"

His cynical laughter sent chills racing down her spine. "You ruined it this afternoon when you met with Mark. He knew the terms. He agreed to them, signed on them, accepted funds already. There was no reason for you to involve yourself. Instead of turning to me, you did exactly what you wanted, even though you knew I'd disapprove."

He looked at her with such coldness and contempt that she felt he was someone she didn't know. It was as if he'd turned a switch, shut down his emotions. The closeness between them was totally gone.

"I don't trust you anymore, Maggie, and frankly, I don't like you very much, either."

She didn't speak to him again during the flight. His harsh rejection left her numb and speechless. On one hand she understood his anger. But on the other, it frightened her that he could withdraw so completely.

They arrived in Healdsburg in the middle of the night. Wordlessly Nic showed her to the master bedroom, depositing her luggage at the foot of the opulent bed.

"But this is your room," she protested.

"Our room," he corrected. She felt a moment of hope. Perhaps there could be some reconciliation. He dashed her hope in the next breath. "We're married, and we'll appear united. However, for now I'll take one of the guests rooms at the end of the hall. I'll tell Francesca you're not feeling well."

He turned at the door. "Except when we entertain, I won't be sharing meals with you. I think it's better to distance ourselves—"

"Yourself, you mean," she interrupted in a passionate burst, finding it impossible to remain quiet or contain her hurt. "I don't need space. I don't want to be apart from you."

"You should have thought of that earlier."

She couldn't bear him to be like this, not after their beautiful wedding and the paradise-perfect honeymoon. She knew what it was like to be loved by him.

Meg went to him, put her arms around him, pressed herself to his chest. "Please, Niccolo, please. Let's not go to bed like this. I can't bear to have you angry with me!"

He held himself rigid. His muscles felt like steel bands beneath her fingertips. His harsh expression didn't relent. "I can't be with you now, Maggie. I'm sorry."

"No, *I'm* sorry. Forgive me!"

He pushed her arms down, propelled her back a step. "I'm tired. I'm angry. I can't talk to you about this anymore. I'm sorry things have turned out this way, but maybe it's for the best."

Her eyes clouded with tears. "Why don't you just divorce me and get this sordid deal over?"

"Because it's not an option."

Of course. Niccolo took his vows with utmost seriousness. He'd never act in passion. "What will we tell my parents?"

"There's nothing to tell. We're married. We're home. The honeymoon—" he hesitated, shrugged most eloquently "—is over."

Truly, she thought dispiritedly, climbing into bed alone fifteen minutes later, the honeymoon was over.

For the next week he slept down the hall in the guest room Meg had used. She heard him come and go at night, saw the light shine beneath his door, but she never spoke to him.

They never shared the same meal, table or room. Niccolo walked out when she walked in. He averted his eyes, drawing back his body, as if she were tainted or possibly contagious.

Meg returned to work at the Hunts', grateful to have the chance to escape the villa. She liked focusing on something other than Nic and her disastrous marriage. Work helped her forget the internal chaos, but only a little, and as one week stretched into two, her anger turned into quiet, silent sadness.

Francesca pretended that nothing was amiss. She chattered cheerfully with Meg, going out of her way to fix her special snacks and fresh fruit drinks. But Meg's appetite was gone. She ate for the baby's sake, and not much more.

Two weeks turned into three, and still Nic avoided her. Once, downstairs, passing the library, she bumped into him as she walked, her head buried in the morning's paper. Nic caught her arm as she reeled backward.

"Nic!" she said in surprise. His hand on her arm felt strong, achingly familiar, and his skin smelled heavenly, like sweet ripe grapes, earth and sunshine.

He righted her and stepped back. But it was the silence that followed that completely unnerved her. He looked at her as if she were a stranger. No tenderness in his eyes. No warmth in his expression.

"How are you?" she asked, folding the paper and tucking it beneath her arm.

"Fine. And you?"

"Fine."

He nodded, yet his mouth frowned. "Have you seen the doctor lately? You're looking thin again."

"I'm supposed to see him tomorrow."

"Do you want me to drive you—" He stopped himself, didn't finish the sentence. His jaw tightened, a nerve popping against the tautness of his skin. "I shouldn't have offered. I already have…something…scheduled."

It was a fib. He had nothing scheduled. He didn't want to be with her.

She forced herself to smile even though her heart ached, the pain almost too intense to bear. "Mom's going with me," she said, creating a fib of her own. But maybe her mother could go with her. They could make a day of it. Have lunch. Do some shopping.

"Good. I'm glad you won't be driving alone." Then he walked away, moving quickly as if she'd already detained him too long.

As Meg watched his hasty retreat, tears burned her eyes. A lump the size of her fist sealed her throat. Niccolo, she was beginning to realize, had no intention of forgiving her.

The next month passed in an exhausting blur. The baby was indeed getting bigger, and Meg's back began to ache from all the hours she spent sitting. To compensate for the long hours at the Hunts, she enrolled in a prenatal exercise class at a local fitness center.

But despite the instructor's constant exhortations to clear the mind, to forget everything but breathing, Meg couldn't banish Nic from her thoughts.

She remembered the honeymoon off the coast of Naples, remembered the eroticism of their time together. Nic had made love to her with tenderness and passion. There had been an urgency in his hands and mouth, a driving force in his sinewy body. She knew he found her desirable, and yet there was more to it than sex and orgasms. Nic held her as though she were infinitely rare, fragile and beautiful.

In his arms she felt...loved.

Weeks continued to pass, and Niccolo remained as distant as ever. As if sensing the discord, her parents made fewer visits, trying to give Meg and Nic time to sort things out for themselves. Meg didn't have the heart to tell them that the extra time and space only made her lonelier.

One Friday, Nic left a scrawled message for Meg that he'd be away for the next several days.

It was late afternoon, and the weekend loomed ahead endless and empty. She couldn't bear being alone another minute, and she picked up the phone, called her mom and asked if she could join them for dinner.

Her mother was delighted, and Meg changed into a sweater and maternity jeans before driving to the ranch.

Golden sunlight washed over the white Victorian farmhouse, highlighting the last of the fall roses. The leaves on the maple glowed red, burgundy and gold. A grapevine wreath hung on the front door.

Home.

And for the first time since Jared had died, there was no pain, no remorse, nothing but warmth. Maybe she and Niccolo would never sort their problems out, but at least Niccolo had made it possible for her to come home again.

Her mom had made Meg's favorite meal, pot roast and mashed potatoes with glazed baby carrots. A fire crackled in the old brick hearth, and after leaving the table, they sat in the family room and played a competitive game of Scrabble. Throughout the game her parents kept the conversation going. They talked about the baby, the crops her dad was considering rotating, her job and the prediction of no rain that month. But they didn't talk about her marriage or her husband.

As Meg finished drying the dessert dishes, her father cornered her in the kitchen. His forehead creased. His toe tapped nervously. "You all right, Maggie?"

She folded the damp dish towel and set it aside. It had been the nicest evening she'd had in a very long time, and she refused to spoil it now. "I'm fine, Daddy."

He stared into her eyes, looking for a sign, for a clue to her emotions, but he didn't find what he was looking for. "I hope you know we love you, Maggie, and we're proud of you. No matter what happens in your life, you can count on us."

Meg wrapped her arms around him. His cheek grazed hers. He smelled of spicy aftershave. Never had she needed a hug as badly as she needed it just then. "Thank you."

"Hang in there, Maggie. I know it seems tough right now. But things always work out in the end."

This coming from a man that had lost his beloved son. Tears filled her eyes. "I love you, Daddy."

"I know you do, baby."

Niccolo seemed to travel constantly. And when he did return he appeared so quietly that half the time

Meg didn't realize he was back. Then, before she could have a word with him alone, he was gone. Board meetings, business meetings, overseas investors, media relations.

The meetings were real, she knew. From what she'd read in the newspaper, the mysterious fungus affecting the red grapes threatened to ruin half the state's vineyards. Niccolo's name consistently appeared in the news reports. He was in the thick of the battle, spearheading funding for research, educating vintners, struggling to calm investors.

She understood on one level but felt totally cut off at another. She'd always known he loved the grapes. His passion for them was nothing new. Only it hurt more now, being his wife and yet being no one, living in his house and yet shunned by him.

She struggled with her emotions, resisting the urge to cry. Tears were useless, she curtly reminded herself, not about to turn morbid in her pregnancy's last trimester. Crying wouldn't repair her damaged relationship with Niccolo, and the baby certainly didn't need the negative emotion. What the baby needed was a nursery, a sweet room to make him feel loved.

Meg ordered a delicate wallpaper and border, and yards of pretty French fabric. With extra time on her hands, she decided to hang the paper herself. Every night, after returning from the Hunts, she ate dinner and changed into her work clothes, a white T-shirt and loose denim overalls.

The work went slowly, but she found it gratifying. After a week laboring in the spacious, high-ceilinged nursery, she'd nearly finished the walls and had one border left to install.

Perched on top of the tall wooden ladder, Meg carefully lined up the border with the thick ceiling crown. Concentrating on keeping the paper straight, she didn't hear the door open.

"What in God's name are you doing?"

Nic's thundering voice startled her, and she nearly fell. Grabbing the ladder to steady herself, she dropped the strip of border tacky with wallpaper paste.

"Look what you did!"

"What I did? I'm not over seven months pregnant balancing on ten-foot ladders!"

"Well, there's no reason to sneak up on me. I'm doing quite nicely without your interference," she retorted, struggling to peel the border off her denims without ripping it.

"I'll give you the count of three to get off that ladder."

"I'm not getting off." Her narrowed glance took in his elegant dress shirt and dark trousers. "Don't you have somewhere important you're supposed to be?"

"One," he said, crossing his arms over his chest and beginning to count.

If he wanted a fight, she'd give him a fight. "Two," she added helpfully.

His glare deepened. "Three. Get off now, before you break your neck!"

"Wouldn't you like that? It'd take care of your most unpleasant commitment."

"Maggie, I'm warning you—"

"Why should I listen to you?" she demanded, tossing the tacky border into the paste bucket hanging from the ladder. "It's been weeks and weeks since our honeymoon, and you've said less than ten words to me. I wake up alone. I eat my meals alone. I go to bed alone. I'm trapped here. And you don't care. You're too wrapped up in your work and your stupid grapes!''

She'd shocked him to silence. It was as if she'd taken the Lord's name in vain. *Stupid grapes.* His mouth hung open. He snapped it shut.

He crossed to the ladder in less than four steps. Reaching up, he unceremoniously hauled her down, holding her against his chest until her feet hit the ground.

Crushed to his chest, her nose buried in the open collar of Nic's white dress shirt, Meg breathed in his cologne. It was her favorite. Citrus and sandalwood.

She closed her eyes, undone by the very smell of him.

He squared her on her feet but didn't immediately let her go. ''Those grapes,'' he said shortly, ''pay our bills.''

She felt his warmth and strength from head to toe, but they only infuriated her. Now it was *their* bills. As if she was part of his life! ''This isn't about money, it's about you. About me. Those grapes matter more to you than anyone or anything.''

''What a typical female response!''

She jabbed her finger into his chest as hard as she could, hitting his breastbone cleanly. ''Sorry, Nic, this time I hit the nail on the head. Dead-on, I might add!''

He pushed her hand away. ''I'm dealing with an industry crisis, and you cry about not spending enough time together!''

''Enough time? Try *no* time.'' She made a circle

with her thumb and pointer finger. "Zilch. Zip. None. But that's what you wanted. This is your way of getting back at me. You're punishing me for making a decision on my own."

"A bad decision."

"It wasn't bad, not if you are Mark's kids."

"My God, Maggie, are we ever going to be rid of Mark?"

He had a point. She knew it. But that didn't excuse his horrible behavior. Worn out, Meg sat on the last rung of the ladder, letting her hands rest on her knees. "I don't know, Nic. All I do know is that this marriage isn't working."

"I won't divorce you, if that's what you're asking."

She laughed softly, without humor. "No, I'm not asking for a divorce. I'm just telling you the truth. This isn't working. And sooner or later something will give."

"I don't have time for this."

"No, you'll never have time. You've got your work waiting for you."

"You make it sound like I have a choice!"

"You do. This disease, even if it kills some of your new Sangiovese grapes, won't bankrupt you. Wines, particularly your new California Chianti, are just a fraction of the Dominici wealth."

"True. My family can afford to weather a crisis like this. But most small wineries can't, and I won't stand by and let my friends and fellow vintners lose everything while I sit up in my big marble villa counting my gold bars."

"No. You'll just leave me in the big marble villa while you chase your precious dream."

"This isn't your dream?"

"No! My dream was us. Us together. Becoming a family." She couldn't stop herself. The words poured out in a rush of feeling. "At least, that's what you told me we'd become. That's what you made me believe would happen."

"What a waste of time!" Niccolo threw up his hands in disgust. "I'm not going to stand here and argue with you. Stay off the ladder. I'll hire someone to finish putting up the wallpaper. And find something else—preferably less dangerous—to keep yourself occupied tonight."

She wanted to shake him. He wasn't listening to a thing she said! "But I don't want to keep myself occupied. I want to be with *you*."

"Hanging wallpaper?"

"Just this last section of border."

"I have a business dinner, Maggie!"

"So, miss the cocktail hour. Skip the appetizers. You can go right after. I'm sure you won't miss the important part of the discussion."

For a moment she thought he was going to relent. His jaw softened, and a small pulse beat erratically at the base of his throat. He reached out and fished a glob of wallpaper paste from a loose curl.

"I would love your help," she added, her voice breaking on the word *help*, "but most of all, I'd just love to be with you for awhile."

In his eyes she saw a longing that matched her own, and she realized with a jolt that he missed her maybe even as much as she missed him. But he wasn't going to bend, and he wasn't going to forgive. Niccolo and his pride.

"Truth or dare?" she whispered, willing him to

play with her. Willing him to move beyond his anger and their feud.

Nic hesitated, swallowed, then turned away. His voice was hoarse when he spoke again. ''I can't, Maggie. I have to go. Just stay off the damn ladder, all right?''

CHAPTER TWELVE

TOO guilty to focus on the business discussion, Niccolo toyed with his butter knife. She was right, he knew she was right, and that only aggravated him more.

He'd been treating her abominably. If it were anyone but Maggie, he would have forgiven him or her by now. But since it was Maggie…

Nic gave his head a small shake, flipped the butter knife onto its blade.

Well, if he wanted to push her back into Mark's arms he was certainly doing a good job. She didn't hate him yet, but she would soon.

He remembered how she begged him to stay, remembered the softness in her eyes, the need in her voice. But instead of listening, instead of caring, he'd walked away. Quite the noble thing to do, hmm?

His cellular phone rang, and it was Francesca. She sounded hysterical. "Slow down," he insisted, leaving the table to take the call in the restaurant's quiet hallway.

Francesca could barely get the words out. Maggie was hurt. She'd gone into labor. An ambulance had been called.

Nic left the restaurant immediately, forgetting to even excuse himself. His heart pounded as he drove the forty miles at record speed. Ten miles from the hospital the freeway turned into a logjam, traffic snarled for miles, red taillights shining as far as he could see.

He was trapped, trapped with his guilt, trapped in the traffic, trapped when Maggie truly needed him.

But then, she'd needed him for a long time, and he'd shut her out anyway, telling himself his work commitments were pressing, pretending that his vineyards were more important than she was. As if his grapes, even his Sangiovese, could ever rival Maggie!

God, what a rotten husband he'd been so far.

Feeling utterly helpless, Nic dialed the hospital's number and requested information on Maggie's condition. But the hospital wouldn't divulge any details over the phone.

"I'm her husband, for pity's sake!" he snarled. *A lousy husband,* a voice rang contemptuously in his head. *Just like you were a lousy friend.*

"I'm sorry, Mr. Dominici, hospital policy. I can tell you that your wife is in her room resting now."

Resting. But what about the baby? "She's pregnant. Is the baby all right?"

"I'm sorry, hospital policy—"

"Yes, I've got it. Thank you."

He reached the hospital three hours after he left the dinner meeting. His nerves were shot, and his mind raced, imagining a hundred horrible scenarios.

After checking in at the nurses' station, he was immediately shown to Maggie's private room. She'd been sleeping, but she stirred at the sound of the door opening.

"Nic!" she whispered groggily, her long dark curls loose over her shoulders, her cheeks pale. She tried to lift her head but lay back, overwhelmed by the effort.

"Did you...have you...?" His voice roughened. "The baby?"

"Fine. So far. The contractions have finally stopped." She managed a wry smile. "Sorry about interrupting your meeting. Wasn't my intention."

God, had he really made her believe his business was more important than her health? Or the baby's life? But thank God Maggie had tried to joke with him. It gave him hope.

Her bright blue eyes met his, and he walked closer to the bed, his heart in his mouth. She looked so small with the medical equipment around her, an IV drip line, a big-screened monitor. "What's that?" he asked, nodding at the green screen.

"A fetal monitor. They're keeping tabs on the baby. Making sure my contractions don't start again."

He smoothed her dark silky curls from her forehead. "I'm sorry, Maggie, I'm sorry for putting you through hell recently."

"You're positively medieval. You know that, don't you?"

"It's one of my faults."

"You make it sound like a virtue."

He smiled rather weakly. Then he caught sight of her wrist. It was bruised and swollen, dark blue smudges circling the slender bones. "So what exactly happened?"

"I was hanging the rest of the border—"

"You were on that ladder?" He saw her small nod. "Even after I told you—"

"Old habits die hard."

"Yes. I know." And he did know. He'd spent two months trying to get her out of his system, with miserable results. He rubbed the back of his neck, gazed at her wide blue eyes and pale face. "I'm not going to change you, am I?"

"No." She reached up and touched his face, her fingers tracing his lips. "But I love you so much the way I am, I hope you won't ask me to change."

"You love *me*?"

"Of course. Why else would I marry a brute like you?"

His lips pursed. "Because I made you."

"Since when have you made me do anything I don't want to do?" she demanded.

Suddenly the rocks he'd stacked around his heart shifted, exposing his feelings. He wanted her, loved her, needed her. "You're impossible."

"I know. You've said that since I was twelve."

She looked so utterly vulnerable, yet beneath the fragile exterior lay the heart of a tiger. "Tell me again about the baby. The doctors have run tests? They're sure he'll be okay?"

"I'll have to take it easy for a few days, maybe a couple weeks. Otherwise, there's been no serious harm." She sniffed, and suddenly tears trembled on her thick black lashes, her eyes darkening to sapphire. "I shouldn't have been on that ladder. I knew it was reckless, but I was so angry with you!"

"My fault," he said, sitting on the edge of the bed and gently drawing her into his arms. She curved against his chest, held on to his coat. "Don't cry," he murmured, kissing the top of her head and smoothing the curls from her damp cheek. "I can't bear it. God help me, Maggie, but I'm a miserable man without you.''

She'd imagined the words, imagined him saying them. He couldn't have meant them. Could he? She looked at him, lightly touched his mouth. "Say it again, please."

His mouth curved, a mocking smile. "What? That I'm lost without you, the most miserable man in the world when you're not with me?"

"Go on."

"That saving your skin means more to me than saving my silly grapes?"

"They're not silly grapes."

"No, they're *stupid*."

Her nose wrinkled. "Sorry."

"I deserved it. I've treated you terribly. And really, all I wanted tonight was to be with you. Hanging wallpaper." He grimaced, his mouth contorting. "Dominicis don't hang wallpaper. But to be honest, nothing sounded better than getting the baby's room ready with you."

"Then why didn't you stay?"

He didn't immediately answer, and then he sighed, deep, heartfelt. Painful. "Pride."

"I thought so."

"Forgive me, Maggie. Forgive me for being arrogant and prideful. Foolish and unthinking. Tonight when I was stuck in traffic, I thought I'd go crazy, worrying about you, worrying about the baby. *Our* baby."

"You really care about us?"

"Care? Maggie, I've been obsessed! I've worried constantly that you'll change your mind, return to Mark, move back to New York."

"You didn't exactly make me *want* to stay."

"No, I'm sure I wouldn't win any awards for hospitality."

"Or congeniality."

His mouth curled. "You're enjoying this, aren't you?"

"Yes. You look lovely eating humble pie."

He laughed softly. When he spoke, his voice was husky. "Maggie, what am I going to do with you?"

"Love me," she whispered, clasping his head and drawing his mouth to hers. At the warmth of his lips, she felt a wave of intense need sweep through her. She'd forgotten what it felt like being nestled in his arms, forgotten the peace she found with him.

"I might not show it very well, but I do love you, Maggie. I love you so much my heart hurts."

"That's a lot of love," she gently teased, holding on to him as if she'd never let go. "So what happens now?"

"I take you home where I can wait on you hand and foot—"

"*You* wait on *me*?"

He grinned shamefacedly, his expression boyish, his golden eyes gleaming. "All right, Francesca waits on you hand and foot, and I adore you from afar."

"I don't think I like the sound of that, either. I want you close, very, very close. I don't think I can bear sleeping in the master bedroom one more night without you."

"You won't have to. I'm not sleeping anymore now that I'm out of the bed."

"You do have comfortable beds," she said with mock seriousness.

"Yes, but it's the irresistible wife that interests me." He kissed her lightly, tenderly, careful not to hurt her or the baby. "I love you, Maggie," he murmured against her mouth. "I love you more than anything, and I can't wait until the baby comes. It'll be wonderful to finally be a family."

"Do you really mean that?"

"With all my brutish heart." He kissed her nose, her brow, her temple. "And I've been thinking about names for the baby. How does Jared sound to you?"

Her heart leaped, and her throat closed. In that moment she realized Niccolo knew her better than anyone in the world.

She struggled to smile through misty tears. "Perfect," she whispered, wrapping her arms around him. "It sounds absolutely perfect."

MILLS & BOON®

Makes any time special™

Mills & Boon publish 29 new titles every month. Select from...

Modern Romance™   Tender Romance™

Sensual Romance™

Medical Romance™   Historical Romance™

MAT2

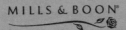

Modern Romance™

THE DEMETRIOS VIRGIN *by Penny Jordan*

Andreas Latimer was Saskia's boss—and he'd just added a clause to her job description. For the sake of his Greek family, she was to play his fiancée!

TO BECOME A BRIDE *by Carole Mortimer*

From the start Danie clashed with Jonas Noble because he was so secretive. But she also found him incredibly attractive—which made her plan to discover his motives even harder! And far worse was the secret *she* was hiding…

THE IRRESISTIBLE TYCOON *by Helen Brooks*

Kim was ecstatic when tycoon Lucas Kane offered her a job—until she realised her new boss was irresistibly sexy. How could she stay true to her vow of avoiding an office affair—especially when Lucas clearly wanted more than temporary passion?

THE UNLIKELY MISTRESS *by Sharon Kendrick*

Sabrina and Guy meet in Venice—the attraction is instant, all-consuming. For one passionate night Sabrina forgets her humdrum life—and then she accepts Guy's invitation to stay with him in London…

On sale 2nd March 2001

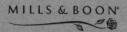

MILLS & BOON®

Modern Romance™

A VENGEFUL DECEPTION by Lee Wilkinson

At first Anna is unsuspicious when she is stranded alone with Gideon Strange. But then she senses the ruthlessness beneath his handsome face and begins to wonder if he has another agenda...

MORGAN'S SECRET SON by Sara Wood

To Morgan, Jodie's visit was worrying. On paper she was the baby's next of kin—but Morgan knew he was the real father. Unless Morgan acted, Jodie would get custody and he would lose his precious son. But the attraction between them was explosive...

EXPECTING HIS BABY by Sandra Field

Lise knew all about ruthless airline tycoon Judd Harwood—but he needed a nanny for his daughter, and against her better judgement Lise took the job. She wasn't intending to spend a night of blazing passion in his bed...

THE TWENTY-FOUR-HOUR GROOM by Laura Anthony

Truman West needed someone to act the part of his wife and Katie Prentiss was the perfect candidate. But he hadn't anticipated how easily Katie would slip into the role—nor had he foreseen the passion that consumed him for this woman!

On sale 2nd March 2001

Available at most branches of WH Smith, Tesco, Martins, Borders, Easons, Volume One/James Thin and most good paperback bookshops

0201/01b

FREE!
4 Books
and a surprise gift!

We would like to take this opportunity to thank you for reading this Mills & Boon® book by offering you the chance to take FOUR more specially selected titles from the Modern Romance™ series absolutely FREE! We're also making this offer to introduce you to the benefits of the Reader Service™—

★ FREE home delivery
★ FREE gifts and competitions
★ FREE monthly Newsletter
★ Books available before they're in the shops
★ Exclusive Reader Service discounts

Accepting these FREE books and gift places you under no obligation to buy; you may cancel at any time, even after receiving your free shipment. Simply complete your details below and return the entire page to the address below. *You don't even need a stamp!*

YES! Please send me 4 free Modern Romance books and a surprise gift. I understand that unless you hear from me, I will receive 6 superb new titles every month for just £2.49 each, postage and packing free. I am under no obligation to purchase any books and may cancel my subscription at any time. The free books and gift will be mine to keep in any case.

P1ZEB

Ms/Mrs/Miss/Mr ....Initials.........................

BLOCK CAPITALS PLEASE

Surname...

Address..

....

....Postcode ....

Send this whole page to:
UK: The Reader Service, FREEPOST CN81, Croydon, CR9 3WZ
EIRE: The Reader Service, PO Box 4546, Kilcock, County Kildare (stamp required)

Offer not valid to current Reader Service subscribers to this series. We reserve the right to refuse an application and applicants must be aged 18 years or over. Only one application per household. Terms and prices subject to change without notice. Offer expires 31st August 2001. As a result of this application, you may receive further offers from Harlequin Mills & Boon Limited and other carefully selected companies. If you would prefer not to share in this opportunity please write to The Data Manager at the address above.

Mills & Boon® is a registered trademark owned by Harlequin Mills & Boon Limited.
Modern Romance™ is being used as a trademark.